FABULOUS Whales

and Other Marine Mammals of Eastern Canada

Graphic Designer: Patrice St-Amour
Scanner operator: Mélanie Sabourin
Illustrations: Réjean Roy
Editor: Michael Ballantyne
Copy Editor: My-Trang Nguyen

Cover:
main photo : humpback whale
insets:
left: Atlantic white-sided dolphin
center: harp seal
right: harbor seal

EXCLUSIVE DISTRIBUTORS:

• For Canada and
  the United States:
  MESSAGERIES ADP*
  955 Amherst St.
  Montréal, Québec
  H2L 3K4
  Tel.: (514) 523-1182
  Fax: (514) 939-0406
  * A subsidiary of Sogides Ltée

• For France and other countries:
  VIVENDI UNIVERSAL PUBLISHING SERVICES
  Immeuble Paryseine, 3 Allée de la Seine
  94854 Ivry Cedex
  Tel.: 01 49 59 11 89/91
  Fax: 01 49 59 11 96
  Orders: Tel.: 02 38 32 71 00
                 Fax: 02 38 32 71 28

• For Switzerland:
  VIVENDI UNIVERSAL PUBLISHING SERVICES SUISSE
  P.O. Box 69 - 1701 Fribourg, Switzerland
  Tel.: (41-26) 460-80-60
  Fax: (41-26) 460-80-68
  Internet: www.havas.ch
  E-mail: office@havas.ch
  Distribution: OLF SA
  Z.I. 3 Corminbœuf
  P.O. Box 1061
  CH-1701 Fribourg
  Orders: Tel.: (41-26) 467-53-33
                   Fax: (41-26) 467-54-66

• For Belgium and Luxembourg:
  VIVENDI UNIVERSAL PUBLISHING SERVICES BENELUX
  Boulevard de l'Europe 117
  B-1301 Wavre
  Tel.: (010) 42-03-20
  Fax: (010) 41-20-24
  http://www.vups.be
  Email: info@vups.be

For more information about our publications,
please visit our website: www.edhomme.com
Other sites of interest: www.edjour.com •
www.edtypo.com • www.edvlb.com •
www.edhexagone.com • www.edutilis.com

Government of Québec – Tax credit for book publishing –
Administered by SODEC.

The publisher gratefully acknowledges the support of
the Société de développement des entreprises culturelles
du Québec for its publishing program.

We gratefully acknowledge the support of the Canada
Council for the Arts for its publishing program.

We acknowledge the financial support of the Government of
Canada through the Book Publishing Industry Development
Program (BPIDP) for our publishing activities.

Canadian Cataloguing in Publication Data
Ouellet, Marie-Claude
  Fabulous whales and other marine mammals from
  Eastern Canada
  Translation of: Fabuleuses baleines et autres
  mammifères marins du Québec
  1. Marine mammmals – Saint Lawrence, Gulf of.
  2. Whales – Saint Lawrence, Gulf of.
  3. Whale watching – Quebec (Province).
  4. Wildlife viewing sites – Quebec (Province).
  I. Title.
QL721.5.S24O9313 2002   599.5'09714   C2002-940445-2

Legal deposit : second quarter 2002
Bibliothèque nationale du Québec

ISBN 2-7619-1722-7

Marie-Claude Ouellet

FABULOUS *Whales*

and Other Marine Mammals
of Eastern Canada

Translated from the French by My-Trang Nguyen

LES ÉDITIONS DE
L'HOMME

This book is dedicated to the
scientists and photographers
who have spent their lives
demystifying those fabulous
creatures called marine mammals.

Tail of humpback whale

Harbor seals

Killer whale

A FASCINATING *World*

Preceding pages:
Harbor seals take advantage of low tide to lounge on the rocks.

A Fascinating WORLD

Since time immemorial, humankind has been fascinated by those enigmatic creatures, our marine mammals. As long as 4000 years ago, stone carvings of whales were found in Norway. Because of their huge size, whales were once regarded as monsters; in fact, the word "cetacean" - from the Greek word, *ketos* - means marine monster.

The sudden appearance of a humpback whale charms this spectator.

Scottish legend has it that seals can turn into human beings once they reach dry land. For their part, the ancient Greeks and Romans, were seduced by the beauty and grace of dolphins. These mammals not only adorned coins, vases and the walls of temples, but also figured as heroes in countless fantastic tales. Thus the Greek musician and poet Arion was saved from drowning by a dolphin. For the early Greeks, killing a dolphin was tantamount to murder.

Thanks to the enormous size of its esophagus, the sperm whale is the only cetacean capable of swallowing a human. Tales abound about sperm-whale hunters being devoured alive. In Herman Melville's classic novel, "Moby Dick," Captain Ahab sought revenge against the elusive white whale that had severed his leg.

Whales also play an important role in the mythology of Canada's native people. Countless art objects depicting whales, seals and walruses attest to the importance of marine mammals

Roman fresco depicting dolphins.
British Museum, London.

Despite its unjustifiably ferocious name, the killer whale is relatively easy to train.

in Inuit culture. According to a Haida legend, a tribal chief on the Pacific coast transformed himself into a killer whale in order to protect his tribe against whale attacks, while a Micmac legend recounts the adventures of Glooscap, a mighty spirit who crossed oceans on the back of a whale. Arriving at his destination, Glooscap offered his sacred pipe to the whale as a token of gratitude. Ever since, legend has it, whales blow "smoke" through their nostrils each time they surface.

Inuit sculpture representing the goddess Edna with a narwhal.

FROM JONAH TO MOBY DICK

According to the familiar biblical story, the prophet Jonah was thrown overboard by sailors after their ship ran into a storm. The unfortunate Jonah was swallowed by a whale, and remained inside the belly of the beast for three days before he was regurgitated, still alive, near a beach.

A friendly pod of bottlenose dolphins, the most common species in captivity. Everyone knows the name of the most famous one: Flipper.

Many of us first discover the wonders of the marine world by visiting an aquarium. What child wouldn't marvel at the acrobatics of a dolphin, or the nimbleness of a sea lion? Thanks to television and movies, marine mammals have become bona fide stars. Still, nothing will fire up your enthusiasm more than an encounter with these creatures in their natural habitat. No doubt that's why millions of people participate each year in observation tours. How can one fail to be moved by the spectacle of a whale surging from beneath the water's surface as if by magic, or forget the look on a seal's face as it peers at you with such obvious curiosity? Memorable encounters such as these make us privileged witnesses to a secret and inaccessible world.

NARWHAL, OR SEA UNICORN

Aerial view of male narwhals in the Arctic.

During the Middle Ages, so-called "unicorn horns" were sold on the open market, much prized for their medicinal properties and use as an antidote. Far from belonging to the legendary white horse, as popularly believed, the "horns" were taken from narwhals. In fact, the narwhal's long, spiraling tusk is actually a tooth.

Christopher Columbus and other early navigators are thought to have confused the pudgy manatees with the Sirens of Greek mythology – those splendid creatures half-female, half-fish.

Swimming with a dolphin is a dream that can come true. There are places in Australia, New Zealand, the Bahamas, the Canary Islands and Florida where you can experience this unique thrill.

The Whales of Saint-Jean

Quebec's folklore is replete with whale stories. The following tale originates in Rivière-Ouelle, a village on the south shore of the St. Lawrence known for its beluga-hunting tradition.

"For decades, a few families in Rivière-Ouelle – to the considerable dismay of neighboring villagers – awarded themselves the exclusive right to hunt white whales in Pointe-aux-Orignaux. It was a practice that made them rich from one generation to another. On one June 24 – the Feast of Saint-Jean-Baptiste – after a particularly abundant catch, they invited families and friends from nearby parishes to come and celebrate the national holiday on the riverbank. At 6 p.m., revelers arrived by the boatload, and soon the entire shore was lit up with campfires. The wine flowed as liberally as the violin music that accompanied the dancing.

The fishing was extraordinary that season, and so the people decided to party all night. All of a sudden, the strains of the music acquired a strange sound; the musicians were unable to control their instruments. Slowly, a thick cloud of vapor rose from the water, enveloping one and all. Then the clouds moved in, from which enormous hands reached out to grasp the revelers. The distraught fishermen hastily gathered their families and headed for their boats. But the hands followed them all the way to the river, trying to overturn the boats. The revelers hurried back to shore as fast they could, then ran to the nearest houses where they took refuge. At that very moment, a huge wave washed over the shore, stirring up whale bones and debris, lifting them into the air in an unholy racket. As the dust settled, hundreds of fiery-eyed white whales could be seen returning to the sea, carrying malevolent, whip-brandishing creatures astride their backs."

Preceding page:
From April to December, Forillon National Park in Quebec's Gaspé area, is a dream destination for watching whales, dolphins and seals.

Following pages:
The Pointe-des-Monts lighthouse, on Quebec's Côte-Nord.

Story and illustration reproduced with the kind permission of Jean-Claude Dupont, author of "Loups-garous, diables et fantômes" (Les Éditions GID, Sainte-Foy, 2001).

LIVING *Submarines*

CHAPTER ONE

Living SUBMARINES

Whale, porpoise, elephant seal, dolphin, sea lion... It's not always easy to distinguish between the various species that make up the world of marine mammals. Today, they are classified in three scientific orders: cetaceans, pinnipeds and sirenians. Cetaceans include toothed whales (killer and sperm whales, porpoise, dolphin) and baleen whales (blue, right and humpback whales). There are over 80 species of cetaceans.

A blue whale's blow is loud and forms a narrow column of vapor roughly 9 meters high.

True Blue Torpedoes

In antiquity, dolphins and whales were believed to be large fish, although certain scholars of the day – Aristotle among them – clearly understood that animals that breathed air and suckled their young could not be considered as fish. In the Middle Ages, Christians, for their part, were fond of feasting on cetacean roasts during Lent. It wasn't until the 18th century that taxonomists began to classify dolphins and whales as members of the cetacean order. The largest animal ever to exist on earth is the blue whale, a cetacean. It can reach a length of 33 meters – virtually the length of a Boeing 737 – and weigh 190 tonnes – the combined weight of 30 elephants. Its heart alone is the size of a compact car. Next comes the fin whale, which can reach a maximum length of 27 meters, and 85 tonnes. These two peaceful giants inhabit the St. Lawrence River and the waters around the Atlantic provinces.

Pinnipeds comprise seals (18 species, including elephant seals), eared seals (14 species, including sea lions) and walruses. Compared with cetaceans, they are more modest in size. The largest pinniped is the Southern elephant seal. It can grow up to 6.5 meters and weigh 4 tonnes. (By itself, the blue whale's tongue weighs as much.) Manatees and dugongs belong to the sirenian order.

Marine mammals are remarkably well adapted for aquatic life. All are endowed with a streamlined, hydrodynamic

A school of dolphins gliding through water at top speed provides a delightful spectacle.

shape, ideal for gliding smoothly through the water. Practically none of their organs – fins excepted – protrude. Testes are internal, the penis is retracted inside the body (except during erection) and the mammillae are hidden in a mammary pocket. For species with pinnae or external ear flaps, the latter are glued to the head and pointed backward so as not to hamper movement. What's more, the skin of cetaceans is extremely smooth, conveniently lubricated and virtually hairless, further enhancing forward motion.

The blue whale beats all rivals in terms of size; it is far heavier than the largest known dinosaur.

SEAL OR SEA LION?

Seals (right) differ from sea lions (left) in that they lack external ear flaps – notice the small hole on the side of their head.

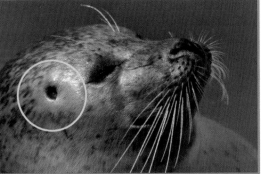

This Hooker sea lion can walk and run by supporting its body on all four limbs.

Whales and dolphins are superb swimmers. They propel themselves by beating their tails up and down, rather than from left to right as fish do. The powerful tail muscles are so solidly attached to the vertebrae that you can suspend a whale weighing several tonnes upside down with no risk of severing the tail. To move about in the water, cetaceans resort to their fore-flippers, which also serve as stabilizers. The dorsal fin, for its part, protects them against body roll. Certain species, such as the beluga, the narwhal and the right whale, lack a dorsal fin. Like porpoises, dolphins frequently jump clear of the water when swimming fast, breathing easily while maintaining speed.

Close-up of a harbor seal's hindflippers.

The word "pinniped" means feet modified into flippers, and refers to those animals that can move both in the water and on dry land. In the water, sea lions beat their webbed foreflippers to propel themselves, using their hindflippers, which are also webbed, to steer and maintain balance. For their part, seals swim with their hindflippers and steer with their foreflippers. Certain seal and sea lion species also jump clear of the water like porpoises. When it comes to moving on dry land – where pinnipeds must go to molt, whelp and feed their young – sea lions have the advantage over seals, using all four limbs to advance. On rough terrain, they can even outrun humans. Seals, on the other hand, crawl rather than walk – by hitching the foreflippers forward.

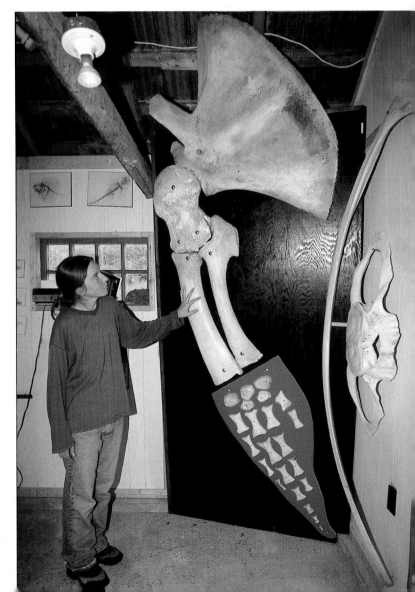

The skeleton of a whale's fore-flippers resembles a human arm and hand. These fin whale bones provide a clear idea of the animal's colossal dimensions.

Bones

The bones and spinal column of land animals need to be strongly resistant so as to support body weight. Not the case for aquatic animals, whose bodies are borne by water. Their skeletons are relatively light, although a blue whale skeleton still weighs more than 22,000 kilograms, as compared to 11 kilograms for a human. Cetacean bones are fragile, consisting of a thin layer of compact outer material covering a spongy inner mass.

After a storm, walrus bones are often washed up along the shores of the Îles de la Madeleine. Until the mid 19th century, these shores were strewn with thousands of walruses. The species was almost exterminated by European hunters, avid for their meat, hides, blubber and ivory.

Fin whale skeleton, at the Musée océanographique de Monaco.

"Thar She Blows!"

Cetaceans breathe through their "blowholes" –
one for toothed whales, two for baleen whales.
Located at the top of the head, blowholes allow
the whale to breathe freely although it barely
breaks the water's surface; that is, without
needing to lift its massive head. A whale is said
to "blow" when it exhales foul air from its
lungs. Contrary to popular belief, a whale does-
n't spout water. If that were the case, its lungs
would have been filled with water, suggesting
that the animal had drowned. If a whale's ex-
haled breath often looks like a spout, it's because the warm, moist air from its lungs condenses as soon as
it comes in contact with the colder sea air (the same phenomenon occurs when human beings exhale steam in cold
weather).

*As a whale emerges,
its blowholes open to take in air.
They close during dives.*

Occasionally, a whale may exhale when its blowhole is still
underwater, resulting in water spurting into the air, a sight that
reinforces the popular myth. By watching the surface of the
water in order to locate "blows", you can detect the presence
of whales. While the blows of smaller cetaceans like porpoises
are barely visible, those of more imposing species are evident
for miles around, and can even reach a height of 12 meters – a
real bargain for hunters and tourists. A warning to those with
sensitive noses: a whale's blow smells like rotten fish.

HOW DO MARINE MAMMALS SLEEP?

Seals can sleep underwater, staying close to
the surface. Every 20 minutes, they emerge
to breathe, without wakening. Cetaceans, for their
part, sleep on the water's surface, day or night –
their blowholes out of the water. They remain in
the same position thanks to a layer of blubber,
which keeps them afloat, but also by gently beating their flippers. Dolphins sleep with one eye
open and keep half their brain constantly on alert
so they won't forget to breathe.

Dolphins jump from the water with stunning power. To reach a height of 5.5 meters, they must break the water's surface at more than 35 kilometers per hour.

While an ordinary mortal can hold his breath for a minute and a half to two minutes, most cetaceans can do so for about 30 minutes. A sperm whale, on the other hand, can stay submerged for more than 90 minutes, and a northern bottlenose whale for two hours. It's a mistake, however, simply to credit the size of cetaceans' lungs. In relative terms, they are slightly less voluminous than human lungs. (It's worth pointing out that a blue whale's pulmonary capacity can still reach 3000 liters.) The secret lies in the fact that when they emerge to breathe, cetaceans empty their lungs almost completely before refilling them with fresh air. In four seconds, a fin whale exhales and inhales 3000 times more air than a human being. Pinnipeds empty their lungs before diving, and are therefore free of all compressed-air diseases.

In order to remain submerged for long periods, cetaceans and pinnipeds store oxygen in their muscles and blood. (A seal's body contains twice as much blood as a terrestrial mammal of the same size.) They are also astute in expending oxygen. First, their heart rate slows down while underwater – from 100 to 10 beats per minute for a seal, for instance. Secondly, circulation is diverted to vital organs like the brain and the heart, at the expense of the reproductive organs, kidneys, intestines, etc.

Efficient Thermostat

Like all mammals, the marine species, including those inhabiting the polar regions, are hot-blooded animals and need to maintain body temperature. To counter the rapid loss of body heat when they are submerged in cold water, marine mammals carry a layer of insulating fat called blubber under the skin. In pinnipeds, this layer can grow up to 10 centimeters thick, as compared to 15 to 20 centimeters for the blue and sperm whales. Right whales are the plumpest, with a blubber layer exceeding 50 centimeters. The thick, waterproof skin covering several pinnipeds provides extra warmth. Thanks to its blubber and fur, the Weddell seal, for example, can easily withstand temperatures as low as − 40°C. What's more, to conserve precious oxygen, pinnipeds modify their circulation, diverting blood away from the flippers and skin where they lose most body heat. This system is strikingly efficient: the difference between the temperature on the surface of a walrus' skin and its internal temperature can be as high as 24°C. Conversely, during a heat wave, pinnipeds direct the heat surplus to their skin and flippers. Thus in hot weather, sea lions can often be spotted cooling themselves by spreading their flippers in a fan shape, while the skin vessels of walruses are bloated with blood, making their skin turn pink.

This tatty-looking harbor seal is molting. The large clumps of hair it is shedding will be replaced by a new coat to protect the animal against the winter cold.

A Sensory World

Marine mammals live a world that is fundamentally different from ours. Several species spend the greater part of their lives underwater, in the dark. How do they perceive their own environment? Do they see it in color? How acute is their hearing? How keen is their sense of smell? Extensive research has unlocked several of these mysteries.

The eyes of cetaceans are fairly small. A fin whale's eye, for example, is the size of an orange. If proportionate to our own, it would be as large as a basketball. Pinnipeds have much larger eyes. A California sea lion and a gray whale have eyes the same size. Marine mammals generally have excellent vision out of the water. Just watch a dolphin jump to catch a fish from its trainer's hand. Most marine mammals also have excellent underwater vision, except walruses and river dolphins. Inhabiting muddy waters, these two species have poor eyesight and can barely distinguish between day and night. The eyes of marine mammals are well adapted to the soft luminosity of the depths. During dives, the iris opens wide to allow more light

This female harp seal sniffs its newborn in order to imbue it with her smell, a process that will help her identify her young among the thousands of calves claiming their ration of milk on the ice floe.

to enter. On the other hand, when the animal surfaces, its pupil narrows to avoid blinding. The eye of a cetacean or a pinniped is covered with a reflective layer like a cat's – the tapetum lucidum – which permits maximum light to be absorbed. Color distinction is probably not well developed.

The skin of whales or dolphins feels like rubber. Smooth and firm, it is also ultra-sensitive. Several marine mammals – notably those in captivity – love to be stroked and scratched. Theirs is a highly tactile society, cementing all relationships – whether between mother and young or sexual partners – with constant touching and caressing. Pinnipeds in particular are equipped with a highly efficient tactile tool called vibrissae –

Thanks to its whiskers, this seal can easily locate its victims, even in muddy water.

CROCODILE TEARS?

Have you ever noticed the tearful look in seals' eyes when they're out of the water? A seal's eye, like a human's, contains the lachrymal fluid that serves as a lubricant. But while the human eye is equipped with a duct that regularly drains excess lacrymal fluid toward the nose, seals lack a duct, which explains their watery eyes.

Of all marine mammals, the walrus has the most vibrissae, some 600 of them. Seals have 80 to 100 vibrissae, and sea lions between 40 and 60.

or whiskers – which help them orient themselves as well as find food. Sensitive both to vibration and touch, the vibrissae – which grow as long as 48 centimeters in certain sea lions – can detect objects such as a wiggling fish without the need to touch them. If it lacked vibrissae, a seal would have great difficulty capturing its prey, although a great many seals are blind, and perfectly healthy. Cetaceans, on the other hand, have little or no sensory hair. The humpback whale, one of the hairiest species, has approximately 100 whiskers covering its head. They are thought to help the animal assess the abundance of food source – plankton and small fish. If it decides that the food is not plentiful enough, the whale will not waste time and energy filtering large quantities of water.

Cetaceans have an ultra-acute sense of hearing which has tremendous value, especially in the obscurity of the ocean depths where sound replaces image. Certain species like the dolphin, the beluga and the humpback whale communicate by using a highly diversified vocal repertory. Toothed whales – and perhaps also baleen whales – have the ability to emit sounds in order to locate food and avoid obstacles. This is called echolocation. Some scientists believe that pinnipeds also practice echolocation. What's certain is that these animals can hear extremely well, below the water or above, harp seals, for example, produce sounds that can be heard as far away as two kilometers underwater. Most pinnipeds are loquacious: they bark, howl, grunt and roar.

Little is known about marine mammals' sense of smell or taste. The latter seems more developed in cetaceans than in pinnipeds. A seal's tongue has few taste buds. It is possible that whales use their taste buds to assess the salinity of seawater, and to sense the various substances contained in the urine and excrement of their own kind. The olfactory sense seems to play a more important role in pinnipeds than in cetaceans. During the mating season, seals and sea lions emit strong odors. That is how a male animal determines the moment when a female is ready to mate. Females use their sense of smell to identify their progeny.

Aerial view of the island of Harrington Harbour, on Quebec's Basse-Côte-Nord. In February or March, thousands of harp seals give birth on the ice just off the island.

Following pages:
Sand Top Bay, on Anticosti Island, offers an exciting panorama.

The picturesque village of Harrington Harbour, Quebec, founded in 1871, is decorated with wooden gangways, which connect one small house to another.

Baffling
BEHAVIOR

CHAPTER TWO

B a f f l i n g   B E H A V I O R

Why do certain whale species strand themselves in groups on the shore? What makes seals swallow stones, or humpback whales sing? These and other marine mammal behaviors continue to fascinate and baffle us. Although research has revealed many facets of their existence, much remains shrouded in mystery.

A killer whale devours anything that moves – except humans: fish, squid, seals, sea lions, walruses, birds, dolphins, whales, polar bears, etc. It can swallow 23 kilograms of food in one gulp.

Dinner's Served!

Whales spend a great deal of time and effort hunting for food. Summer is the time when they eat the most, consuming between 3 and 10 percent of their body weight every day. For the rest of the year, their food intake is reduced tenfold, as they rely on their reserves of fat in order to survive. Contrary to popular opinion, the waters containing the most nutrients are those situated near polar regions, a fact that explains why scores of whales generally "fill it up" in cold waters – the St. Lawrence River in particular – during the summer. Feeding habits vary according to species. Toothed whales, or odontocetes, hunt their prey one at a time. Rather than chewing their food, they swallow it whole, using their teeth to hold the slippery fish. Toothed whales rely on echolocation to detect their victims, as we'll see later. Certain odontocetes, like sperm whales, hunt alone; while others, like dolphins, pilot and killer whales, hunt in packs, suggesting a keen sense of cooperation. Once a school of fish has been encircled, the whales continue swimming around to keep the fish together as each takes a turn feasting.

Rorquals have ventral grooves that enable them to gulp large quantities of water and food. The term "rorqual" – from the Norwegian ror, tube, and hval, whale – refers to the ventral grooves.

PECULIAR DENTITION

A sperm whale's teeth appear on its lower jaw a full ten years after birth – a fact that suggests the teeth are not needed for eating. The species is believed to capture its prey by suction, possibly after overwhelming them with powerful sonar pulses. The strategy suits the mammal perfectly, enabling it to capture creatures capable of swimming much faster, like those 12-meter long-giant squid.

Sperm whales' teeth are cone-shaped, each weighing more than 500 grams. As with other odontocetes, teeth are all identical.

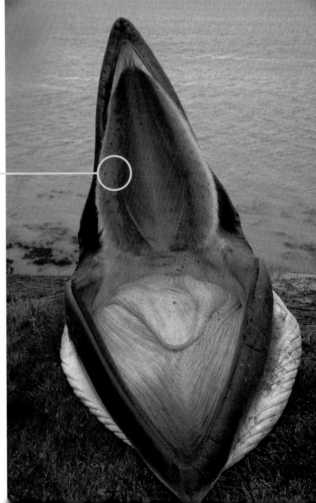

A strande minke whale. Its tongue and baleen hang from the upper jaw. Resembling vertical blinds, baleen plates – like human hair and nails – are composed of keratin.

WHY DO WHALES BREACH?

Some cetaceans like the killer, humpback and right whales, frequently burst out of the water. (A humpback in particular was observed breaching 130 times in 75 minutes). It is believed that the young do so in order to develop their muscles, and the adults to communicate with their own kind. It may also be a way of getting rid of parasites that cling to their skin.

In mating season, humpbacks breach frequently, attracting potential sexual partners – not to mention photographers.

Mysticetes have no teeth. Instead, they use a series of horny plates called baleen, which hang from their upper jaw, to capture small marine organisms. Each mysticete possesses between 400 to 700 baleen plates, depending on the species – those of the Greenland right whale, for example, can grow up to 4.5 meters long. Baleen whales feed exclusively on small preys, on account of their narrow esophagus, which measures only 10 to 15 centimeters in diameter, even in large individuals. Mysticetes are divided into two categories: skimmers and gulpers. Skimmers – which include right whales – feed by slowly swimming with their mouths open near the surface. After passing through the baleen plates, the seawater then drains through a corner of the whale's lips, leaving the food – primarily krill – trapped between the plates. Gulpers use a different tactic. They rush their prey, gulping an inordinate amount of water filled with plankton and small fish. Then they close their mouths and, by contracting certain muscles, release the water through the baleen plates. The throat and the belly of these whales are pleated like an accordion. As the pleats or grooves expand, they form a pocket that, in the case of the blue whale, can hold 35,000 liters of water (the equivalent of a full-size swimming pool). Oddly enough, the largest animal on the planet feeds almost exclusively on krill, those tiny shrimp-like creatures measuring six centimeters long. An adult blue whale ingests four tonnes of krill per day – roughly 79 filtrations – during the summer. Smaller species must expend even more energy – 355 filtrations for a juvenile minke whale, to obtain its daily 700-kilogram ration of krill. Humpback whales use a highly ingenious feeding method. Once they've spotted a school of fish, they form a circle underneath it, then slowly rise, releasing a constant cluster of bubbles. The bubbles form a kind of corral that encircles the prey as the whales swim toward it with their open mouths.

Krill is the blue whale's favorite food.

The mouth of a humpback whale opens wide to catch food.

Pinnipeds are endowed with approximately 30 sharp teeth used for holding prey. Like cetaceans, they don't chew their food. Small fish are swallowed whole, while larger ones are shredded. Most pinnipeds are opportunists, consuming a variety of food, although some species are a good deal more selective. Walruses, for example, feed mainly on clams, sucking the soft meat before spitting out the shell, while crabeater seals, despite their name, feed almost exclusively on krill, which they filter with their teeth. Crabeater seals were so named when early explorers mistook the reddish debris they had spotted in the seals' excrement for crab remains.

Did you know that some seals swallow stones? Scientists have yet to come up with a satisfactory explanation for the 11 kilograms worth of small stones that were once found inside a seal's stomach. Was it to help the animal chew its food or regurgitate fish bones? Or perhaps to allow it to eliminate the parasite worms infesting its stomach? Theories abound, but the jury is still out.

Sophisticated "Sonar System"

Marine mammals live in a dark environment. Even in crystal-clear water, light barely penetrates below 60 meters. On the other hand, sound travels easily – four or five times faster than in the air – at about 1500 meters per second. Marine mammals know how to take advantage of this fact, using sound to communicate with one another, to navigate, and to detect their victims. Many whales are endowed with a highly sophisticated echolocation system, which functions like a sonar system. Thanks to echolocation, toothed whales (and perhaps also mysticetes and pinnipeds) can locate objects with extraordinary precision, without seeing or touching them. Experiments have demonstrated that killer whales can detect the presence of a ring measuring 10 millimeters in diameter as far as three meters away. Even with their eyes blindfolded, dolphins can distinguish between a wooden picture frame and one made of plastic or metal.

Dolphins use their sonar to move underwater and capture prey.

How does this animal sonar system work? First, imagine a dolphin exploring its environment. It emits high-frequency sound waves – a series of very sharp sounds – in every direction. If these so-called ultrasounds strike an object worthy of interest, the dolphin emits a new set of sound waves – of higher frequency this time – in order to learn more about the object. After hitting the target, the sounds bounce back to the dolphin, providing a highly precise "acoustic image." The animal will then act accordingly – either lunging for an appetizing fish, or avoiding a dangerous reef, as the case may be.

How dolphins send and receive ultrasounds is still a mystery. Most scientists believe that the sounds are produced as a result of air penetrating the animal's respiratory system. (Others speculate that cetaceans are endowed with human-like vocal cords.) These sounds then travel through a fatty bulge – called the "melon" – on the animal's forehead, which acts as an acoustic lens and transmits them through the seawater. As for the echoes sent back by various objects, scientists believe they

ARE WHALES INTELLIGENT?

Dolphins are often said to be more intelligent than dogs, or even humans. The size of a cetacean brain is certainly impressive – a sperm whale's weighs nine kilograms (four times the human brain). But intelligence isn't a concomitant of brain size, but of the use made of it. On this score, whales use a large part of their brains for hearing and touching, As for nerve cells – another measure of intelligence – whales have very few. Nonetheless, how does one account for the fact that in captivity several cetaceans are able to memorize and execute a variety of difficult tricks, not to mention the fact that some of them even invent games to dispel boredom?

Killer whales are among the most intelligent cetaceans. They have no difficulty learning tricks.

are picked up by the animal's jawbones and transmitted through the internal ears to the brain.

Echolocation sounds are generally too high-pitched to be detected by human ears. However, cetaceans also make a variety of discernible noises: they grunt, whistle, bark and roar. The moan of a blue whale, for example, can exceed 188 decibels, compared to the 170 decibels produced by a jet plane. It's not hard to imagine just how frightened early seafarers must have been when they heard those bizarre sounds vibrating through their wooden ships. The role played by vocalization varies according to species. Thus, the melodious chant of the male humpback whale serves to lure females while intimidating its rivals. Sounds emitted by such gregarious cetaceans as dolphins, belugas and pilot whales help maintain cohesion between members of their group. Stray whales vocalize as they attempt to rejoin their own herd, while those stranded or injured use sound as an SOS. And the very low-frequency sounds produced by blue whales allow them to survey the underwater topography. Since these subsurface

Belugas are dubbed "sea canaries," as a tribute to their highly elaborate vocal repertory.

The harp seal emits a variety of sounds, whether underwater or on dry land.

The proboscis of the male northern elephant seal probably serves to amplify the sound when it bellows. Similar to the noise made by a motorcycle with a broken muffler, it can be heard one kilometer away.

sounds can spread for hundreds of kilometers, scientists now wonder whether whales that are 300 to 400 kilometers apart can communicate between themselves, and if they do, how such sonorous messages actually travel. Do they reach their destination intact or in altered form?

Of all pinnipeds, sea lions are the most talkative. The males roar as a way of driving their rivals off their territory. Typically, two adversaries take the measure of each other by adopting intimidating postures and making loud noises. Needless to say, the stronger, louder animal generally prevails. In this way, the animals solve their conflicts without serious risk. For their part, male walruses belt out a strange vocal mixture of barking, grunting and whistling to seduce females. Several species make use of unique calls in order to strengthen the bonds between mother and young. When a sea lion returns from fishing to feed her pup, she must find and identify it – first by the sound of its voice, then by its smell – among the thousands of calves sprawled over the beach.

Mating

It's virtually impossible to tell the difference between a male and female whale. The male's testes are internal and the penis retracted inside the body; the female mammillae are hidden in a skinfold (except during feeding). And the chances of examining a whale's belly are virtually nil. Fortunately, certain external characteristics – the size of the animal, for one – are revelatory. Female toothed whales are slightly smaller than the males; while among the large rorquals, the opposite is the case. The gender of killer whales is easier to spot, thanks to the highly visible dorsal fin – the female's is curved backward like a shark's. The same goes for the narwhal, whose long spiraling tusk is normally an exclusively male feature. Pinnipeds normally display many signs of sexual dimorphism. The male elephant seal, for example, sports a long proboscis and weighs three times more than the female. For their part, male sea lions sport a flowing mane. In certain pinnipeds, you can distinguish the sex by the color of their skin.

This harp seal is just a couple of hours old. Pups under five days old are called "little yellows" because their skin is stained with amniotic fluid.

The hooded seal courts females by inflating its nasal membrane, This bright red ornament can grow to a diameter of 15 centimeters.

During breeding season, male walruses often fight violent duels.

Cetaceans and pinnipeds attach great importance to mating rituals. Parades are often spectacular. The humpback and the right whale are particularly exuberant. They slap the water's surface with their tails and flippers and even jump clear of the water. The harp seal and walrus are equally demonstrative. The former jumps and swims at full tilt to impress the females, while the latter seduces its companion with bell-like sounds, accompanies her when she dives, and rubs her whiskers with his own. This species, like several other pinnipeds, is polygamous. Males usually fight among themselves for supremacy. In any given breeding season, a male elephant seal may copulate with hundreds of females.

North Atlantic right whales mate in herds. The female is surrounded by a handful of males who vie for her attention and favor. The animals roll over each other, swim in circles and dive in unison. When the female consents to mate, she approaches a potential male, presses her belly against his, then starts the process all over again with a second suitor, then a third. Dolphins are more discreet. They caress and nibble one

WHAT DIET?

Whale's milk feels as thick as concentrated. It's highly nutritional, thanks to its generous fat content (up to 40%) and protein. By comparison, cow's milk contains 90% water and 3 to 4% fat. With such rich food, no wonder a young blue whale gains three to four kilograms per hour. For the record, the calf ingests 40 kilograms of milk per day, representing more than 370,000 calories — a world away from the daily 1800-calorie human diet. Seal's milk feels like mayonnaise. The hooded seal produces the richest milk, containing more than 50% fat. During its four-day feeding period, a seal calf gains seven kilograms per day.

Female hooded seal feeding its one-day old calf. After four days, the calf will be weaned and abandoned.

another, then execute an elegant underwater dance. Copulation among cetaceans is extraordinarily short, lasting between 5 and 20 seconds.

Most cetaceans breed in their favorite habitats. Some 300 North Atlantic right whales, for example, mate and calve each summer in the Bay of Fundy, off the coasts of New Brunswick and Maine. Other species do so in the tropics, like the humpbacks, which migrate from the Atlantic to the Caribbean in the fall, near the Dominican Republic. For most cetaceans, gestation lasts from 10 to 12 months, a fairly short period, considering their size. Sperm and pilot whales are the exception: their pregnancies last 15 to 16 months. Fetal development is phenomenal. A blue whale fetus weighs almost two tonnes during the last months of pregnancy. Most cetaceans give birth to one calf at a time. The smaller species breed every year while others do so every three to five years. Cetacean calves are born tail-first. At birth, the mother – often assisted by other females – quickly brings her infant to the surface so it can take its first breath. Its size is imposing: a newborn blue whale, for instance, measures seven meters in length and weighs 2.5 tonnes. A calf doesn't automatically suckle, so its mother must contract some muscles to force the milk into the mouth

Brown at birth, baby belugas turn blue-gray after a year or two, and entirely white at age seven.

of her baby. The feeding period varies between a few months to two years, depending on the species, although certain sperm whales are not weaned until they reach the age of 15.

Pinnipeds generally breed in spring or early summer. Some give birth on dry land, others underwater. Like cetaceans, pinnipeds bear one pup at a time. In most species, the fertilized embryo stops developing for several months, a phenomenon known as delayed implantation that allows for the synchronization of whelping and mating activities. In this way, the males can take advantage of a large concentration of females at a time when the latter are most sexually receptive – that is, following the birth of their babies. Birthing generally takes less than a minute, which leaves little time for the newborn pup to acclimatize itself. Needless to say, the shock is immense as the pup transfers from a warm womb temperature of 37°C to the – 10°C cold outside, deprived of insulating fat and covered only in its downy fetal hair – called the lanugo. To keep warm, it has no other choice than to shiver. Furthermore, its body can burn "brown fat," a process which generates a lot of heat. Baby seals can save energy by sleeping for long periods. A baby harp seal, known as a "whitecoat," has an extra asset: it's covered with transparent hairs through which sunrays can reach its heat-retaining dark skin. Even in 0°C weather, the temperature of a whitecoat's skin can stay as high as 41°C.

The bond between mother and young is strong in marine mammals like the beluga, dolphin, walrus, gray and sperm whales. The calves swim and play all around their mothers, even occasionally resting on their backs. Female sperm whales jealously guard their young. While a female dives to feed, another looks after her calf, protecting it against sharks and killer whales. A baby walrus usually stays two to three years with its mother, who ferociously defends it against all predators.

A female spotted dolphin and her calf. The pair will live together for several months, swimming in the clear, warm waters of the southern Atlantic.

Humpbacks usually give birth every two years.

Long-Distance Travelers

Certain marine mammals migrate long distances in order to take advantage of better feeding and reproductive conditions, generally spending the summer in polar regions and the winter months in warmer waters. Several cetaceans calve in tropical waters, so their young can be protected against colder temperatures.

California gray whales are the longest migrators, logging up to 18,000 kilometers every year. They feed in the Bering Sea in summer, then travel south to lagoons along the coast of Baja California (Mexico) to shelter and breed in winter. Experts believe that their brains are equipped with magnetic crystals, enabling them to detect the earth's magnetic field and thus orient themselves. The harp seal is another great traveler, typically totting up more than 5000 kilometers per year between the Canadian Arctic and the Îles de la Madeleine, in the Gulf of St. Lawrence.

Ice formations in regions like the Arctic, the Labrador Strait and the Gulf of St. Lawrence greatly influence the seasonal distribution of marine mammals and their food sources. All are aware of the danger of being locked in by ice. That's why harbor seals typically migrate to waters where currents and tides keep them ice-free.

A rare photo of a blue whale feeding in the Gulf of St. Lawrence, in winter. It will stay there so long as it finds enough food.

The gray whale often raises its head vertically from the water, perhaps to look around and orient itself.

INDIVIDUAL STRANDING

In general, an individual cetacean, stranded by itself, is either old, injured or sick. It may also have made a navigational error — while pursuing food fish, for example — which led it into shallow water.

This juvenile minke whale stranded itself on Île Verte in 1996. Despite attention and care, it perished a few hours later. Its inexperience may have caused it to have been caught at low tide.

The Mystery of Stranded Whales

Why do tens, even hundreds, of cetaceans occasionally run aground only to die on the shore? This intriguing phenomenon has a long history. According to the ancient Greek historian, Plutarch, it was a kind of collective suicide. But more plausible explanations have been advanced since then. While some incidents may be due to natural causes, others are linked to human activity. A disturbance in the earth's magnetic field – caused by a magnetic storm, for example – may very well disorient the cetaceans, causing them to commit fatal navigational mistakes. Moreover, some scientists believe that sound waves produced by ships and submarines can effectively scramble the mammals' own guidance system, which may help explain the increased incidents of mass strandings following naval maneuvers. Another theory involves the natural behavior of social species like dolphins and pilot and sperm whales. When one of these cetaceans strands itself, so the theory goes, it typically puts out distress calls to its own kind, luring them to their own deaths. To prevent this mass slaughter, scientists sometimes resorted to drastic measures such as killing the first stranded animals before they could put out distress calls, hoping that the survivors would return to the sea. The strategy actually worked, saving between 150 and 200 white-sided dolphins, stranded in Florida in 1974. Although mass strandings of cetaceans are considered rare, 10,000 such incidents have been recorded since 1913.

Pilot whales often fall victim to mass strandings; hundreds are regularly found along the coasts of Newfoundland.

After a storm, muddied waters can interfere with the cetaceans' sonar system.
The Îles de la Madeleine, in the Gulf of St. Lawrence, are notorious for violent storms.

Following pages: *The picturesque village of Rivière-au-Tonnerre, on Quebec's Côte-Nord, bathed in sunlight.*

FIRST AID

A stranded whale may die of dehydration, starvation or – in the case of very large species – be crushed by its own weight. In fact, organs like the heart and lungs are highly compressed by the enormous body mass. The animal dies slowly, the agony sometimes lasting two or three days. Should you ever find a stranded whale that is still alive, contact fisheries department officials immediately. While waiting for the experts to arrive, stay away from the tail and speak calmly to the animal. If the mammal is resting on its back, make it roll over in order to clear its blowhole so it can breathe. Keep the skin moist by sprinkling water on it, then covering it with damp cloths. First-aid workers may try to put it back in the water, by pushing it on its side or at the base of its dorsal fin. In any case, don't get your hopes up. Even after such treatment, cetaceans will often strand themselves again.

Endangered
SPECIES

Preceding pages:
*When will oil tankers be required to have double
hulls to minimize the danger of spills?*

CHAPTER THREE

Endangered SPECIES

Victims of careless slaughter over the years, several marine mammals such as the blue and right whales and the Guadalupe fur seal have come close to extinction. Others, like the Caribbean monk seal and the Atlantic gray whale, are virtually non-existent today. During the last three centuries, whales were hunted mercilessly.

*This beluga was hunted in the
St. Lawrence River in the early
years of the 20th century.
In 1915 alone, 900 belugas
were slaughtered.*

Killer whale feasting on a young minke, photographed near Mingan, in the Gulf of St. Lawrence.

In 1966 alone, 66,090 animals – a record number – were killed around the world. Although interest in whaling has subsided since the 1980s, the survival of these magnificent creatures is far from assured. New dangers, such as chemical and noise pollution, accidental entanglement in fishing nets and collision with ships, threaten their existence.

In their natural environment, marine mammals have few predators. Yet danger is never far away – sharks and polar bears, for instance, feed on small cetaceans and seals. Ironically, the marine mammals' principal enemy is a member of their own kind: the killer whale. This formidable hunter attacks seals, sea lions, dolphins, small walruses, and even large cetaceans like the sperm and blue whales.

On an Arctic fox's menu: baby seals, among other items.

Hunting

So far as marine mammals are concerned, man is unquestionably their worst enemy. Early hunters were probably content simply to recover stranded animals on the beach. Later, they took to hunting them with rudimentary weapons such as nets and hand-held harpoons. For centuries, the Inuit hunted whales, seals and walruses in this way, exploiting every body part: fur and skin, of course, but also meat, fat, bones, teeth, sinews, baleen plates, tusks. The raw materials were used to make clothes, tools, weapons and decorative objects. Blubber was used for cooking and as fuel for oil lamps. In fact, were it not for marine mammals, the Inuit could not have survived their harsh, inhospitable environment.

Stationed beside a seal hole, this polar bear waits patiently for the seal to come up for air.

THE RARE NARWHAL

For early Inuit, the narwhal was a valuable source of raw material. Tusks were used for sleigh runners and harpoon tips, sinews for sewing shoes, garments, kayaks or for making harpoon lines and harness for sled dogs. They also appreciated the animal's dark meat, not to mention its crunchy, hazelnut-tasting skin (*muktuk*), containing more vitamin C than citrus fruit.

Nowadays, Canada's native people hunt the narwhal for its meat and skin, but mostly for its ivory, which has great value on Asian markets. A narwhal tusk – which in 1978 fetched $1000 per meter – can grow over three meters in length and weigh more than 10 kilograms. However, hunting quotas have now been imposed to protect the species, and both the United States and EEC countries ban the importation of narwhal ivory.

The Basques and Norwegians were the first to hunt whales commercially, around the year 1000. Basque hunters were especially keen on the right whale, which possessed a double advantage over other species: they swam slowly and after they died, the carcasses stayed afloat, thanks to their high fat content. (In the 19th century, whalers inflated the carcasses of other whale species with air to keep them afloat, making recovery easier.) After virtually decimating whale populations in the Bay of Biscay, whalers ventured to higher latitudes – notably Greenland, Newfoundland and Labrador, as well as Grandes-Bergeronnes and Île aux Basques in Quebec. During the 16th century, one of the most important whaling stations in the world was located at Red Bay in Labrador. It's not hard to imagine the origin of the name. The fearless Basque whalers pursued the giant beasts aboard small rowing boats, killing them with hand-held harpoons, then towing the

Killer whales are natural and fearless hunters.

carcasses to dry land in order to melt down the blubber for oil, leaving trails of blood in the water. At summer's end, the whalers brought the precious oil back to Europe, where it was used mainly for lighting purposes.

In 1712, New Englanders were the first to hunt sperm whales on a commercial basis, so successfully that by the 1860s their numbers had decreased dramatically. The sperm whale provided unique raw materials: spermaceti and gray amber. Spermaceti is a solid substance found in the sperm whale's head and was used for making candles and industrial lubricants. (Eventually, it was used in the automobile and space industries.) Gray amber forms in the intestine of the sperm whale. Foul-smelling when fresh, it was nonetheless an ingredient in the manufacture of perfume. Once properly

Workman slicing whale blubber.

During the 1900s, about 75 whales were processed annually at the whale-oil factory in Sept-Îles, Quebec.

In Sept-Îles, whalers operated aboard small steam boats.

refined, however, it produces a pleasant musky fragrance.

In 1868, the whaling industry was revolutionized by the advent of the harpoon cannon, invented by a Norwegian sea captain named Svend Foyn. The powerful weapon fired grenade-tipped harpoons that detonated inside the body of the whale. Thanks to the harpoon cannon, fixed to the bow of a steam-powered boat, whalers could pursue even the fastest-swimming whales, firing at them from a distance. At the turn of the 20th century, another innovation – the factory ship – almost wiped out what was left of the whale population. Whalers were now able to winch the carcasses onto ramps on board the vessels, dismember them and process the blubber on the spot. The blue whale – most prized of all – was the factory ship's main target. Its population fell so dramatically in the 1950s that hunting was banned in 1965. Concerned about depleting stocks, the International

Whaling Commission (IWC) imposed a moratorium on commercial whaling altogether in 1986, although some countries like Norway, Russia, Japan and Iceland still continue the hunt, within more or less sustainable limits. Today, many environmentalists suggest that dolphins and other small cetaceans are still not adequately protected.

Canada banned commercial whaling in 1972. Although it was never a major competitor like Norway, Great Britain, Holland, the United States, Japan and the former Soviet Union, Canada once maintained its share of whaling stations, principally in Nova Scotia and Newfoundland. Species hunted included the sperm and northern bottlenose whales, minkes, fin and pilot whales. During the "good years," from 1951 to 1961, 4000 pilot whales were taken, their meat used in raising mink. In Sept-Îles, Que., a whale-oil factory was in operation from 1898 to 1913. The oil was used for making margarine, while meat waste and bones were converted into manure. For 300 years, belugas were hunted in Quebec for their meat, oil and hides. Resistant and virtually waterproof, beluga hides were used for boots, shoelaces, automobile seats

ALL-PURPOSE BALEEN PLATES

Baleen plates were a valuable commodity in the old days. During the 19th century, at a time when a sailor earned a mere 26 cents per day, they fetched over $6 a kilogram. Flexible and resistant, the plates were used for making hairbrushes, floor brooms, springs, hats, umbrella ribs and even those well-known instruments of torture known as corsets.

Baleen plates drying in the port of San Francisco.

Workers wear studded boots as they dismember a slippery whale.

and luggage. Belugas were trapped by means of weir-like enclosures, made of rows of sturdy poles planted near the shore. Commercial beluga hunting was banned in 1979.

Thanks to a range of protective measures, pinnipeds are far less endangered than cetaceans. In fact, several species have had excellent opportunities to replenish themselves. The northern elephant seal is an extraordinary case in point. In 1890, they numbered between 20 and 100. Following hunting bans imposed by the United States and Mexico, their population has climbed to more than 100,000. However, certain pinnipeds – the harp seal in particular – are still commer-

During whaling expeditions, seafarers kept boredom at bay by engraving landscapes, portraits or scenes of daily life on whale teeth and bones.

WHALE ON THE MENU

In Japan, whale meat is considered a delicacy, fetching hundreds of dollars per kilogram. DNA analyses have revealed that some restaurants even served the meat of such protected species as the blue and humpback – illegally, of course.

Whitecoat molting. Only a clump of white hair – memento of its original fur – still remains. After 12 days, when all its white fur has been shed, the pup is fair game for hunters.

cially pursued. When seals gather in great numbers during breeding season, they are easy prey. In the 18th century, 33 million harp seals are thought to have been killed around Newfoundland. Even today, they are the most hunted species in the Gulf of St. Lawrence. Fortunately, their population numbers more than five million in the Gulf and the northern part of Newfoundland. Adult harp seals are valued for their fur, skin, meat and oil, the latter being used for cooking, and for making lubricants and cosmetics. On the other hand, whitecoats (baby seals) have been spared since 1983, the year the European Economic Community (EEC) banned Canadian seal fur. This decision had been spurred by protests by animal activists who protested the killing of baby seals with clubs.

Other Dangers

Hunting aside, several other human activities unwittingly put the lives of marine mammals at risk. The presence of ships, for one, increases the danger of collision as well as accidental spills of toxic products. Marine traffic also disturbs the mammals' habitat scrambling their sonar and echolocation systems. The North Atlantic right whale is the world's most vulnerable. Scientists observe that almost half of the 300 that still inhabit North Atlantic waters bear the scars of collision with ocean-going vessels. To reduce these risks, the states of Florida and Georgia have implemented air surveillance to warn ships of whale movements. The program has been so successful that its implementation is being considered for the Bay of Fundy, a vital breeding area for whales.

Generally speaking, fishermen and marine mammals don't get along. Each year, thousands of seals and cetaceans are caught in fishing nets and drown. Even species with sophisticated echolocation systems cannot detect nylon netting.

This blue whale drowned after it was caught in a fishing net.

The tail of this humpback was severed by a ship's propeller.

Collision with motorboats is the primary cause of death for Florida's manatees.

Between 1960 and 1990, more than six million dolphins are believed to have died in this manner. Since 1990, tuna fishermen have used a special type of netting as well as other techniques designed to spare dolphins. In Canada, the Whale Research Group in Newfoundland and Labrador has developed an acoustic alarm device – installed on fixed fishing gear – to help the animals detect and avoid the gear. The device has been credited with reducing the risk of collision between whales and codtraps by 70%.

Fishermen are known to complain that certain marine mammals (seals, killer whales) not only damage their nets, but devour bait as well as the catch. In the past, some charged that belugas consumed such valuable fish stocks as cod, salmon, halibut and redfish. Acting on these concerns, the Quebec government inaugurated a 10-year program in 1928 designed to reduce the number of belugas in the St. Lawrence

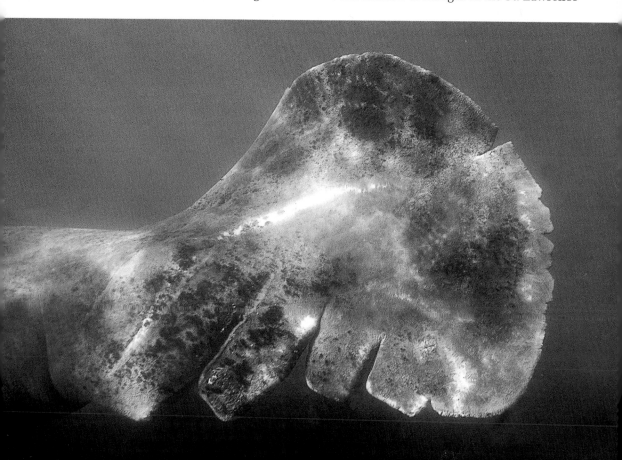

River, offering bonuses and even carrying out aerial bombardments. Later it was found that belugas actually consumed little of the valuable fish. Today, fishermen demand that quotas be increased for culling harp and gray seals. But because seals feed on herring, which eat cod roe and larvae, scientists are concerned that the cod population will be harmed by reducing the number of seals. It is imperative, therefore, that authorities proceed with caution if they want to strike a proper balance between various marine populations.

Chemical pollution presents the most insidious threat for marine mammals. Substances such as hydrocarbons, PCB, PAH, DDT, mirex and mercury, are systematically dumped into the oceans. Animals inevitably ingest these pollutants, storing them in their blubber. In the Baltic Sea, for example, pollution has killed many seals and caused infertility in others. In Canada, scientists are concerned about the high rate of contamination in harbor seals, harbor porpoises and belugas. Autopsies carried out in the last two decades have demonstrated that belugas suffered from various diseases, including cancer, that are linked to chemical pollution. Their population went from 5000-10,000 at the start of the 20th century, to 1000-1400 today.

The gash on the side of this blue whale was caused by a collision with a ship. About 20% of blue whales in the St. Lawrence bear similar scars.

"Dolphin Safe" logo on some tuna-can labels

Aquatic animals face other dangers as well. An ordinary plastic bag can be fatal for a seal or a whale, if they mistake it for a jellyfish and swallow it. Once inside, the bag will block the animal's digestive system, and be fatal.

The St. Lawrence beluga is a symbol of all endangered species.

Preceding page: Canada's lighthouses operated on whale oil until the 1860s, when it was replaced with the more economical kerosene. Above is the lighthouse at Peggy's Cove, N.S.

Following pages: The Skyline Trail in Cape Breton Highlands Park offers imposing panoramas.

VIAGRA TO THE RESCUE

The Chinese believe that a seal's penis can cure male impotence. To supply this market, thousands of seals were killed in the past.

The advent of Viagra changed everything. Now the male organ, which fetched $100 in 1996, is worth a mere $15.

THE WORLD OF
Cetologists

Preceding pages:
*This modern-day bowman is
about to conduct a whale biopsy.*

CHAPTER FOUR
The World of
CETOLOGISTS

The study of marine mammals in their natural habitat is no picnic. Imagine yourself on board a research boat, waiting hours on end for a whale to surface, and then only for a brief moment. A career in cetology, therefore, calls for infinite patience. So what exactly motivates scientists to spend years observing creatures that spend the vast majority of their lives underwater, far from inquiring eyes? Doubtless a passion for discovery.

Belugas in the St. Lawrence hold almost no secrets for biologist Robert Michaud, director of the Group for Research and Education on Marine Mammals (GREMM) in Tadoussac, Quebec. For the past 15 years, Michaud has studied the distribution and social habits of beluga whales, not to mention the ecology of the great whales and the impact of whale-watching cruises on the mammals themselves.

Family Portraits

But there are also tantalizing issues that pique the curiosity of those zealous researchers. What do whales do in the ocean depths? How do they communicate? Where do they go in winter? To interpret the snatches of data they've been able to glean on the surface, scientists have developed various research tools, some at the cutting edge of technology.

To the untrained eye, all whales of the same species look alike. An expert, on the other hand, can instantly tell individuals apart, by checking certain distinctive traits such as color, the shape of dorsal fins or tails, and the presence of permanent scars. Cetologists photograph the animals they observe, assigning a name or code to each. From this information, they compile a catalog of hundreds of identity cards, complete with photographs. This process is known as photo-identification. Thanks to the catalogs, experts from different countries can exchange vital information on marine mammals, particularly as regards their migratory patterns. The humpback whale was one of the first species to be photo-identified, as it is fairly easy to recognize. You need only examine the underside of its tail as it lifts up just be-

A humpback whale can be distinguished from its kind by the different color patterns under its tail.

fore the animal dives. It carries patterns that are as unique and distinctive as human fingerprints. When a whale lifts its tail, a cetologist has a split second to make an identification. The catalog of North Atlantic humpbacks features more than 4000 individuals, or roughly 80% of their current population. Thanks to photo-identification, we now know a fair amount about the humpbacks' migratory movements.

Since 1986, GREMM has focused on belugas in the St. Lawrence, photo-identifying as many as 200 individuals. Although the mammals can be recognized by their color and scar patterns, some stand out on account of their behavior. An individual called Galubé, for example, has always been intensely curious about passing ships – a rare character trait for an adult beluga. By studying the identity card of each catalogued beluga, cetologists learn more about its habits, breeding success and relations with other members of the species. GREMM has also compiled a catalog of some 50 fin whales.

Richard Sears, founder and director of the Mingan Island Cetacean Study (MICS), is a pioneer in blue whale re-

Cetologists occasionally name a whale after the shape of a spot or scar on its body. Grand Galop [Gallop Along] refers to a fin whale with a spot shaped like a rocking horse behind its dorsal fin. Le Bossu [Humpback], for its part, can be recognized by a large hump next to a long scar on its back.

search. In the late 1970s, Sears was the first cetologist to conduct long-term studies of blue whales, identifying them by the speckles on their sides. To date, he has identified some 350 individuals living in the St. Lawrence, from Grandes-Bergeronnes to Blanc-Sablon, Quebec. He also studies blue whales in Iceland and in the Sea of Cortez, Mexico.

WANTED: ADOPTIVE PARENTS

As a means of financing their research, several organizations now offer the public a chance to adopt a whale. In return for a donation, the "adoptive parents" get an adoption certificate, complete with photo and data about their whale. GREMM's "Adopt a Beluga" program, started in 1988, has been wildly successful. Some 100 belugas have been adopted by various schools, municipalities and corporations. MICS also started its "Adopt a Blue Whale" program in 1988, while the ORES Centre for coastal studies in Grandes-Bergeronnes, Que., led by zoologist Ned Lynas, lets you adopt a minke.

DNA Secrets

Until recently, it was inconceivable even to consider the genetic study of marine mammals. To begin the process, you must first carry out a biopsy, in other words, extract a few milligrams of the animal's skin and fat. The sample is obtained by means of a crossbow that shoots a sterilized, hollow-tipped dart. Whether this operation is painful for the animal is anyone's guess. But judging from the fact that several whales return to their previous activity soon after the biopsy – which lasts only a few seconds – it's safe to assume that they are not disturbed. Considering the valuable information a biopsy can provide, experts deem that the benefits far outweigh the risks. However, some researchers prefer using a scoop to collect fragments of skin that have fallen off naturally, rather than resorting to a biopsy. By analyzing a specimen's DNA, we can discover, among other data, the animal's sex, its level of contamination, and its biological relationship with other individuals. Biopsies have been carried out on a number of harbor seals in the St. Lawrence in order to determine their position in the food chain and individual levels of contamination.

Since 1984, MICS scientists have been following a group of four killer whales off Mingan Island. Of the four, Jack Knife (in the background) is the easiest to identify. This male was named after the unusual shape of its dorsal fin, which looks like, well, a jackknife.

As the Crow Flies

Pilot whales often travel in groups of 10 or more.

Counting cetaceans and pinnipeds is generally done from an aircraft or helicopter. The task can be tricky, especially when the weather turns foggy, rainy or windy. Because marine mammals are often gray-colored, they blend into the watery landscape. In addition, some species may not surface promptly at census time. Finally there's always the risk of counting the same individual more than once. Aerial inventories, therefore, can be unreliable. Fortunately, some species are easy to count, like California gray whales, because they all pass through the same strait, in Alaska.

Underwater Music

A beluga's repertory includes whistling, bell-like sounds, jaw clicks and squeaks.

Bioacoustics is a science that helps us understand the correlation between whale sounds and behavior. Scientists study these vocalizations by using underwater microphones called hydrophones. Humpbacks' vocalizations are a fascinating research subject. The male sings for hours on end, constantly repeating certain patterns. Each individual belts out a tune that is slightly different than any of the others, and which changes over time. Since the early 1990s, Chris Clark has been eavesdropping on whales, listening to their sounds via a network of once-secret hydrophones installed on the bottom of oceans by the United States Navy to track enemy submarines. By studying the vocalizations of fin and blue whales, Clark was able to establish their respective migratory routes.

Plugged-In Animals

Penetrating the secret universe of marine mammals has long been a scientist's dream. It is now a reality, thanks to the sophisticated transmitters that can be affixed to the animals themselves, and will relay valuable data about their habits – how they move and behave underwater, for instance. But first, how to place the device on the animal? Scientists generally use transmitters with a suction disc, which they position on the animal's back by means of a long pole. The operation sounds simple enough, but it can take hours, since you have to get close enough to the animal in the first place, and that is a tricky business by itself. Once secure, the transmitter will relay data to the computer aboard the research boat. It can remain active for a few hours or even a few days, until it falls off. To install a satellite transmitter, researchers use a crossbow, implanting the device 10 centimeters deep in the animal's fatty tissue. The

This researcher places a transmitter on a hoodel seal.

Telemetry gives researchers a better understanding of the ecology of various marine mammals, including the harbor seal.

transmitter can remain active for a few days at the very least, even as long as a few months, transmitting data via satellite to computers in a research laboratory. Signals may be picked up anywhere in the world, making satellite telemetry an ideal tool for following the movements of marine mammals and studying their behavior over long periods. The information acquired from these two types of transmitter is broad-based, ranging from the mammals' slightest movements, their speeds, the duration and depth of their dives, their body orientation underwater, and so on.

Thanks to these transmitters, biologists now know that harbor seals in the Rimouski region generally dive to depths of less than four meters, and do not migrate far from their main habitat. They are currently considering measures to protect these relatively stationary mammals against harmful habitat disturbances such as chemical and noise pollution.

Biologist Janie Giard and veterinarian Sylvain Deguise nursed Bob every two hours, giving it a milk formula through a syringue and feeding tube.

TO BOB'S RESCUE

In 1991, in Forestville on Quebec's Côte-Nord, the captain of a tugboat spotted an abandoned baby beluga as it swam around his ship. The captain notified local authorities, who quickly took action, giving the two-week-old calf, nicknamed Bob, serum and antibiotics before transporting it by hydroplane to the Aquarium du Québec. Attempts to bottle-feed Bob were unsuccessful, so they had to force-feed the calf. Despite their efforts, Bob died 10 days later of lung failure.

Pollution's Harmful Legacy

According to research scientists Pierre Béland and Daniel Martineau, pollution is particularly harmful to beluga whales, affecting their immune and reproductive systems. Béland and Martineau have studied beluga carcasses for 20 years, performing more than 75 necropsies. They have detected dozens of toxic substances, such as lead, mercury, PCB, mirex and DDT, in the dead animals, and noted an alarmingly high incidence of tumors. Studies of live belugas (complete with biopsies) were started in 1994 to determine whether they, too, were as contaminated as their dead relatives. The studies continue.

Following pages:
A foggy landscape near St. Vincent, Nfld., a renowned observation site for humpback whales.

There are so many contaminants in a beluga carcass that it cannot be disposed of in a garbage dump. It's regarded as hazardous material.

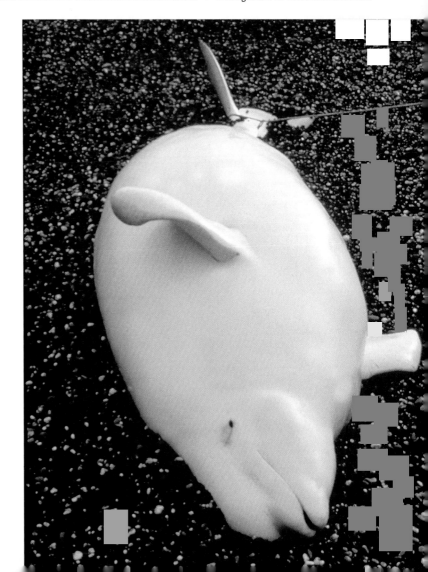

OBJECTS OF
Curiosity

Preceding pages:
*Floating along with a whale on board of a sea kayak
is a memorable experience. Although whales are peaceful
by nature, it's best to err on the side of caution.*

CHAPTER FIVE

Objects of

C U R I O S I T Y

In the mid 1950s whale watching gradually became an organized and popular recreation, spurred by the comeback of the California gray whale, the first species to catch the public imagination. Today, whale watching is a commercial enterprise in its own right, active in some 30 countries around the world. In Japan and Norway, tour operators have converted whaling vessels into observation ships.

Like a giant fan, the tail of a blue whale spreads out above the water, often more than five meters across. But only 15 to 18 percent of blue whales in the St. Lawrence display their tails.

Quebec got into the act in 1971, the year the Zoological Society of Montreal offered its first whale-watching excursion in the St. Lawrence estuary. Until that time, the presence of whales in the St. Lawrence – considered to be one of the best whale-observation sites in the world – was a well-kept secret. Tour operators quickly made up for lost time, however, and by 1983, there were eight whale-watching boats operating on the Côte-Nord, catering to 20,000 tourists every summer. The economic potential seems unlimited, attracting new operators all the time. Today more than 50 whale-watching boats offer excursions in the St. Lawrence estuary, averaging about 300,000 clients annually. The industry generates more than $40 million a year for the Tadoussac region alone. Worldwide, it is worth close to U.S. $1 billion.

Young or old, we all love whales. Here, a pilot whale approaches an observation boat off Cape Breton, N.S.

A Practical Guide

To get the most out of watching these spectacular creatures, choose an outfit that offers the services of experienced naturalists. They will help you identify whales, as well as explain their behavior. As for the type of conveyance, there is a large selection for every budget and taste: sailboats, fishing boats, large vessels, zodiacs, and even hydroplanes. Each type has its own advantage, so your choice should be guided by your expectations and needs. If you like speed and excitement, go for the zodiac, which will make you feel as if you were swim-

TADOUSSAC – A MECCA FOR WHALES

People often wonder why so many whales congregate in the waters around Tadoussac, near the mouth of the Saguenay River. The reason can be found in that particular stretch of the St. Lawrence, which constitutes a prodigious pantry for whales, teeming with such favorite delicacies as krill, fish and squid. The abundance of food is due to tidal movements as well as the area's underwater topography, in particular the deep depression known as the Laurentian Channel, which runs from the mouth of the Saguenay River all the way to the Atlantic. Between Grandes-Bergeronnes and Tadoussac, the riverbed rises dramatically – from 300 meters to 20 meters over a 15-kilometer distance. The icy water from the bottom rises with it, bringing large quantities of nutrients which, under the sun's effects, act as fertilizers and stimulate the growth of microscopic algae. The plants, in turn, feed a host of small fish and invertebrates that eventually end up in the stomachs of other creatures, including marine mammals.

ming along with the whales. On the other hand, your view may be blocked by other passengers. If it's comfort you prefer, then a larger boat will be a better choice. It also provides an unequaled vantage point. From high up on the deck, you can even spot the whales through the clear waters, even before they surface.

Be sure to dress properly. It's always much colder on the water than it is on land. So take along a windbreaker and, if necessary, gloves and hat. Sunscreen and sunglasses are also musts. Other essential items: binoculars and a guide to marine mammals (see pp. 117-150). A little advice: Resist the temptation to capture everything on film, lest you be disappointed by the results. What will you do with 10 out-of-focus shots of a seal's head, or a whale fin that has barely poked out of the water? Wait until the subject becomes clearly visible. And make sure to protect your camera against rain or seawater.

When you embark on a whale-watching trip, it's natural enough to imagine scores of whales breaching, a herd of belugas escorting a boat, or a cavorting school of dolphins. "It was just

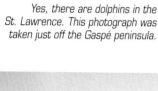

Yes, there are dolphins in the St. Lawrence. This photograph was taken just off the Gaspé peninsula.

like fireworks!" a French visitor exclaimed after witnessing a group of minke whales surging out of the water. This may happen to you, too, but don't get your hopes up, because Mother Nature is capricious. Better instead to be realistic, and avoid disappointment. After all, just being able to get a close-up view of one of those giant creatures in its natural habitat is a thrill all by itself. If a spectacular display is thrown in, so much the better. A word or two about those proverbial tail flukes slicing the surface: While it's true that the humpback, right and sperm whales do raise their tails high in the air before diving, other species, like the minke, don't always do the same thing, because their tails are flexible enough to bend beneath their bodies as they dive. And not all blue whales lift their tails either. To quote a GREMM naturalist: "You're much more likely to spot a whale tail on a billboard than out at sea!"

Before you go, find out which whale species frequent the target area at the time of your visit. For example, blue, fin, minke and beluga whales generally swim in that area of the St. Lawrence estuary between Tadoussac and Les Escoumins, while harbor porpoises, Atlantic white-sided and white-beaked dolphins, humpbacks and pilot whales frequent the Gulf. If you want to see a right whale, the Bay of Fundy is the place to be, while seal lovers should check out Quebec's Côte-Nord as well as the Bas-Saint-Laurent and Gaspé areas. If you're taking your first whale-watching tour, you'll be struck by the frenetic atmosphere that often prevails on an excursion boat. As the first herd of whales surface, the shouting starts, faces light up, and perfect strangers share thoughts and feelings. It's quite magical.

It's always a thrill to watch a seal in its natural habitat.

If You Have Your Own Boat

One way to spot whales is to try and detect their spouts in the distance. To make it easier, experts visualize the boat as a giant clock placed horizontally. The bow stands for "twelve o'clock," the stern "six o'clock," and so on. If you happen to hear, "Spout at four o'clock," there's no need to check your watch.

If you navigate in their habitat, here's how to watch whales without disturbing them. Move at consistently slow speeds and approach the animals at an angle. (A frontal or rear approach may upset them.) Respect the ethical code and don't try to get closer than 200 meters. (But if a whale voluntarily swims close to your boat, by all means take advantage of the situation.) Wait until you are at least 400 meters away from the animal before starting gradually to pick up speed again. If you spot belugas, keep your distance. Do not approach them, or let yourself drift toward them. Although plentiful elsewhere, St. Lawrence River belugas are an endangered population and merit special protection. The use of excursion boats is not encouraged for fear of breaking up a herd, separating mothers from their young, for example, and to reduce the risk of collision. If you're wondering whether a whale can upset a boat, the answer is no – at least so far as oil tankers and large excursion vessels are concerned.

But a whale can accidentally overturn small craft. To avoid any chance of an accident, make sure that whales can see your boat at all times. Do not turn off the engine, keep it on "idle" instead. If you travel by sea kayak, make your presence felt by placing a radio against the hull or by knocking on it regularly. Stay well clear of the animal's tail.

Resembling a giant fin, this iceberg drifts at the mercy of the currents.

Ecotourism or Harassment?

Whales have now become star attractions.

The sight of a single whale encircled by dozens of boats is more commonplace than you may think. But, at the same time, are we running a risk of harming the animals by admiring them so enthusiastically? Because fin whales are a prime target for whale-watching expeditions, GREMM researchers recently undertook a behavioral study of these great mammals to find out whether this kind of public attention was affecting their normal existence. Between 1994 and 1996, researchers equipped 25 individual animals with radio transmitters and spent 382 hours following their movements. They discovered that the whales spent less time underwater (where they normally feed) while in the presence of tour boats. Scientists are concerned lest this will affect the amount of food the whales consume, possibly jeopardizing their health and migratory behavior. The study underlines the need for sensible management strategies regulating the whale-watching industry. In 2001, the Saguenay-St. Lawrence Marine Park mandated that the number of excursion boats be limited to 54. Other countries, such as South Africa, are even more cautious, and have banned whale-watching cruises altogether. If you're concerned about disturbing the animals, or if you suffer from seasickness, why not try observing them from shore? You'll find a map indicating excellent land observation sites at the end of this chapter. Thanks to its white color, the beluga is visible from a distance of several kilometers, and is therefore ideal for land-based observation. As a matter of fact, look-out stations have been set up near Tadoussac and along the Saguenay River for just this purpose. At Cap Bon-Désir, large whales swim relatively close to the shoreline, aided by underwater trenches more than 100 meters deep, which allow the whales to operate comfortably.

Cute Little Whitecoats

After the 1983 moratorium banning the sale of baby-seal fur, a number of seal hunters decided to become "ecotour" guides. Each year, at the end of February or in early March, hundreds of tourists from Europe, Japan and the United States arrive by helicopter on the Îles de la Madeleine icefields to observe the harp seals and their pups. All you need is a strong constitution to withstand the extreme cold, between -20°C and -25°C, and pockets deep enough to fork out the $3000 to $4000 needed for an all-inclusive package. You can easily approach a whitecoat because its mother will immediately dive when she spots a human – unlike the female hooded seal, which fiercely guards her young. So it's best to keep a minimum distance of five meters. And watch out for male hooded seals – they can be aggressive and have sharp teeth and claws.

If you're looking for the best place in the world to find whitecoats, try the Îles de la Madeleine.

Labrador

Havre-Saint-Pierre

Longue-Pointe-de-Mingan •

Île

QUÉBEC
QUEBEC

Sept-Îles •

Parc nationa

Pointe-des-Monts •

Gaspé •

Percé •

Baie-Comeau •

Ragueneau •

Forestville •

Sainte-Anne de-Portneuf •

Les Escoumins •   • Trois-Pistoles
Bergeronnes •

Lac Saint-Jean

Nouveau-Brun
New Brunswick

Tadoussac •

Baie-Sainte-Catherine •

• Rivière-du-Loup

Québec •

St-Andrews

Deer Island
Campobello Island

États-Unis
United States

Grand Mana
Island

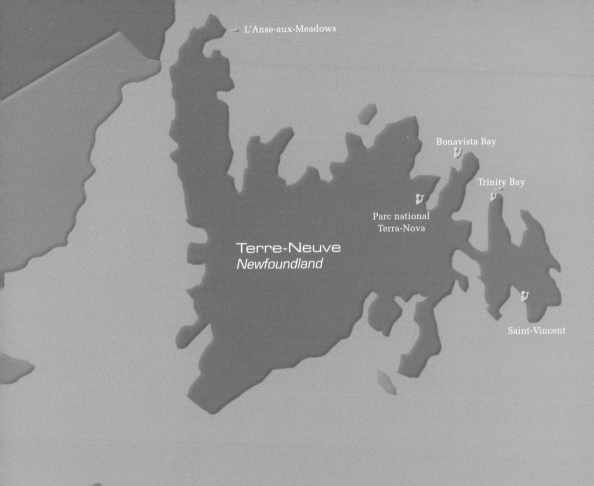

L'Anse-aux-Meadows

Bonavista Bay

Trinity Bay

Parc national
Terra-Nova

Saint-Vincent

Terre-Neuve
Newfoundland

Cape Breton

ure

Brudenell •
Î.-P.-É.   Montague •
P.E.I.   Murray River •

Nouvelle-Écosse
Nova Scotia

igby

Lunenburg

sland

Map of land-observation sites and sea-excursion locations

Most of the listed sites are good places to observe cetaceans and pinnipeds. A pictogram depicting a seal indicates the areas where seal-watching excursions are available.

A MINE OF INFORMATION

Interpretation Centres are excellent sources of information on local marine mammals. Here a few of them:

La Pointe Noire Interpretation
and Observation Centre
(GREMM and Parks Canada)
Baie-Sainte-Catherine, Quebec
Telephones: (418) 237-4383
(418) 235-4703 (off season)

Mingan Island Cetacean Study
(MICS)
Longue-Pointe-de-Mingan, Quebec
Telephone: (418) 949-2845

Red Bay Visitor's Centre
Red Bay, Labrador
Telephone: (709) 920-2197

Marine Mammal
Interpretation Centre (CIMM)
Group for Research and Education on
Marine Mammals (GREMM)
Tadoussac, Quebec
Telephone: (418) 235-4701

Seal Interpretation Centre
Club Vacances "Les îles"
Grande-Entrée, Îles de la Madeleine,
Quebec
Telephone: (418) 985-2833

South Dildo Whaling and
Sealing Museum
Trinity Bay, Nfld.
Telephone: (709) 582-2317

Grand Manan Whale and Seabird
Research Station
North Head, N.B.
Telephone: (506) 662-3804

Whale Interpretive Centre
Pleasant Bay, N.S.
Telephone: (902) 224-1411

Preceding page: *The Mingan Archipelago has fabulous treasures:
crystal-clear water, unusual monoliths and a myriad of birds and marine mammals.*

Following pages: *Near Fatima, Îles de la Madeleine.*

*This humpback whale seems to greet the village of Lourdes-de-Blanc-Sablon, on Quebec's Basse-Côte-Nord,
by wagging its tail. In the Strait of Belle Isle, between Labrador and Newfoundland, whales are an exciting spectacle.*

Identification GUIDE

Preceding pages:
*Despite its 30 tonnes, the humpback whale
is remarkably agile.*

Identification GUIDE

This section presents a checklist of the different marine mammal species that inhabit the waters of the St. Lawrence and the Atlantic Provinces. Each listing includes descriptions of individual animals as well as useful information for whale-watching tours.

The listings are organized under two main headings: cetaceans (odontocetes and mysticetes) and pinnipeds.

*The cliffs at Cape d'Or, N.S.,
overlooking the sea.*

NORTHERN BOTTLENOSE WHALE

SCIENTIFIC NAME	Hyperoodon ampullatus
LENGTH	6 to 10 meters
WEIGHT	3 to 7 tonnes

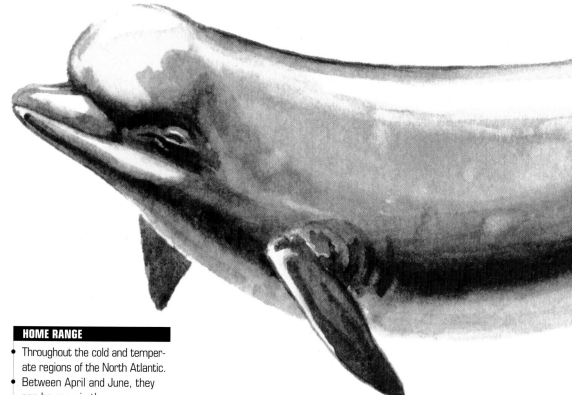

HOME RANGE

- Throughout the cold and temperate regions of the North Atlantic.
- Between April and June, they can be seen in the open sea off the coasts of Nova Scotia, Newfoundland and Labrador. In summer, they move farther north to the Davis Strait. In the autumn, most individuals migrate southward to escape the ice packs.

DURATION OF DIVE

- The northern bottlenose whale will commonly stay underwater for 35 to 40 minutes. One harpooned specimen remained submerged for two hours, a record for cetaceans.

REPRODUCTION

- The female gives birth every 2 or 3 years. After a year-long gestation period, she produces a calf which she suckles for more than a year.

FOOD SOURCE

- Can dive to depths of 1000 meters in search of squid, herring, ground fish (ocean perch, halibut), and sometimes starfish and sea cucumbers.

NATURAL ENEMIES

- Killer whales and some shark species.

SPECIAL FEATURES

- Like the sperm whale, the northern bottlenose whale is a champion diver, reaching depths of up to 1000 meters and staying submerged for up to two hours.
- The whale can jump clear of the water in a complete breach and slap the surface with its flukes, making a terrific racket.
- Curious by nature, the bottlenose will often approach a boat, staying nearby for as long as an hour.
- A small population living off Nova Scotia is threatened by natural-gas drilling operations on Sable Island.

SURFACE BEHAVIOR

- When this whale breaks the surface, its melon and beak appear simultaneously. It often shows its flukes as it sounds. Its balloon-shaped spout can reach a height of 2 meters.

SOCIAL BEHAVIOR

- Gregarious, the whale swims in pods (4 to 10 individuals), but occasionally in pairs or alone. Several hundred animals may assemble to migrate.

DISTINGUISHING FEATURES

- Bulbous head with long jaws terminating in a short beak.
- Back cinnamon brown, paler shade on the belly.
- Sharp dorsal fin, curved backward.
- Two V-shaped grooves under the throat.
- Strong sexual dimorphism: the adult male is considerably larger than the female, its melon development is more prominent and it has two teeth located at the tip of the lower jaw. (Females are toothless). Older males carry a white mark on the forehead.

Northern bottlenose whales rarely venture into the estuary and the Gulf of St. Lawrence. This specimen was stranded at Montmagny in November 1994.

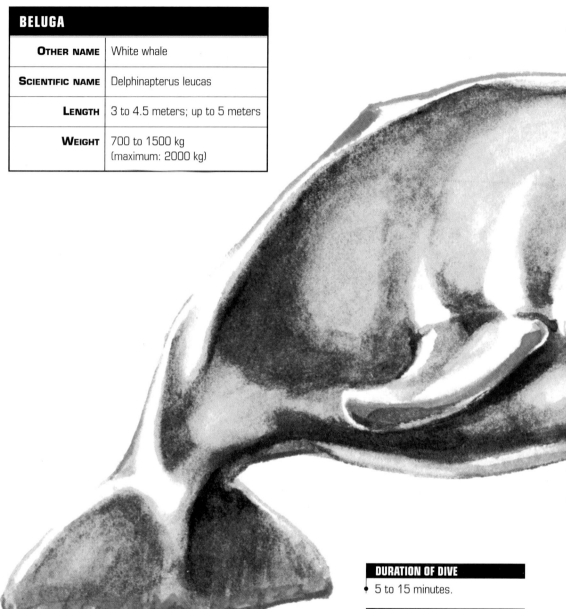

BELUGA

OTHER NAME	White whale
SCIENTIFIC NAME	Delphinapterus leucas
LENGTH	3 to 4.5 meters; up to 5 meters
WEIGHT	700 to 1500 kg (maximum: 2000 kg)

DURATION OF DIVE
- 5 to 15 minutes.

DISTINGUISHING FEATURES
- Adult whales are pure white, while newborns are a dark brown color, and the immature whales are blue-gray.
- Absence of a dorsal fin; presence of a dorsal ridge.
- Fatty protuberance on the forehead, called the melon.

SURFACE BEHAVIOR
- Breathes on the surface two or three times a minute.
- Will show its flukes.
- Swims rather slowly.
- Its spout ("breath") is hard to see but relatively noisy.

FOOD SOURCE
- Very varied. Mainly fish (capelin, sand launce, herring, eels, salmon, cod), but also sea worms, crustaceans, octopus and squid.

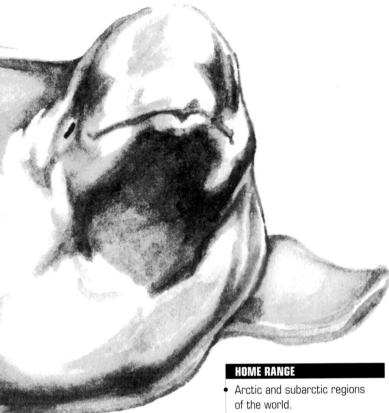

SOCIAL BEHAVIOR

- Very gregarious; often swims in pods (2 to 10 individuals), but sometimes in a herd numbering hundreds of animals. Females and their young form separate groups that move about apart from adult males.

REPRODUCTION

- Gestation lasts 14 months, and calving takes place in summer. Females give birth to a single calf every 3 years.

NATURAL ENEMIES

- Killer whales, walruses, polar bears.

HOME RANGE

- Arctic and subarctic regions of the world.
- The St. Lawrence River belugas are a remnant of the population that inhabited the Champlain Sea 12,000 years ago. The beluga is the only cetacean that stays year-round in the St. Lawrence. In spring, summer and autumn, belugas frequent that part of the estuary located between Île-aux-Coudres and Les Escoumins (north shore) and between Kamouraska and Île-aux-Basques on the south shore. They appear in the Saguenay River as well. In winter, belugas move downstream as far as Pointe-des-Monts on the north shore and Sainte-Anne-des-Monts on the south shore where the ice is broken up.

SPECIAL FEATURES

- The beluga is well adapted to an Arctic environment. Its fat, or blubber, protects it against the cold and its white pigmentation acts as a camouflage among the ice floes. Thanks to its dorsal ridge and the thick skin on its head, a beluga can break a hole through 10-cm-thick ice in order to breathe.
- Nicknamed "sea canary," the beluga emits a greater variety of sounds than any other cetacean.
- The St. Lawrence River population is in danger of disappearance. From some 5000 to 10,000 belugas that lived there at the beginning of the last century, only about 1000 are left, certainly no more than 1400. Initially the victim of commercial whaling, the beluga is today threatened by chemical pollution.

While exploring the St. Lawrence in 1535, Jacques Cartier spotted some belugas and described them as follows: " A kind of fish as large as a porpoise but without a fin, spotlessly white as the snow."

SPERM WHALE

SCIENTIFIC NAME	Physeter macrocephalus
LENGTH	10 to 15 meters; up to 18 meters
WEIGHT	15 to 40 tonnes; up to 50 tonnes

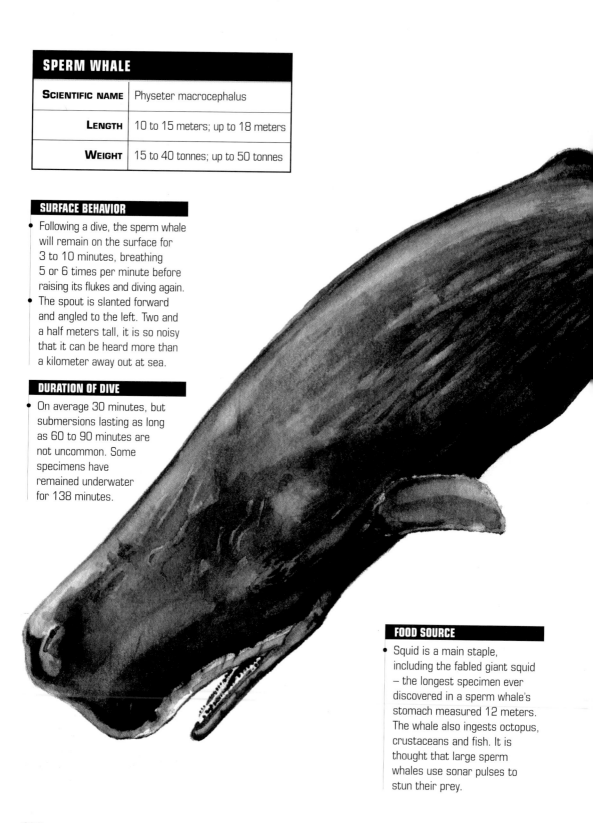

SURFACE BEHAVIOR

- Following a dive, the sperm whale will remain on the surface for 3 to 10 minutes, breathing 5 or 6 times per minute before raising its flukes and diving again.
- The spout is slanted forward and angled to the left. Two and a half meters tall, it is so noisy that it can be heard more than a kilometer away out at sea.

DURATION OF DIVE

- On average 30 minutes, but submersions lasting as long as 60 to 90 minutes are not uncommon. Some specimens have remained underwater for 138 minutes.

FOOD SOURCE

- Squid is a main staple, including the fabled giant squid – the longest specimen ever discovered in a sperm whale's stomach measured 12 meters. The whale also ingests octopus, crustaceans and fish. It is thought that large sperm whales use sonar pulses to stun their prey.

SOCIAL BEHAVIOR

- Gregarious. Normally lives in a group of 10 to 15 individuals, although adult males sometimes travel alone. A sick or wounded sperm whale will be helped by other members of the group.

NATURAL ENEMIES

- Healthy adults probably have no known natural enemies. Only killer whales and some shark species dare to attack a young sperm whale or a sick individual.

DISTINGUISHING FEATURES

- Massive square-shaped head and very small eyes.
- The skin is wrinkled, colored dark gray or grayish brown. The flanks and belly are a lighter shade. Some individuals are completely white, like the legendary whale in Herman Melville's novel, "Moby Dick."
- There is no dorsal fin, but a triangular, low hump followed by a series of raised lumps along the spine.
- The small flippers are located near eye-level.
- There is a single blowhole, on the left side just in front of the snout.

REPRODUCTION

- Mating occurs in the autumn in tropical waters. Gestation lasts from 14 to 15 months. Nursing lasts between 18 to 24 months, but some calves continue to suckle for several years after weaning. The female sperm whale gives birth every 4 to 6 years.
- Males are polygamous and form harems of 20 to 30 females. Violent combat, punctuated by head butts and bites, breaks out from time to time, leaving the belligerents deeply scarred.

HOME RANGE

- Worldwide, favoring very deep water.
- In Canada, they are found off the Pacific and Atlantic coasts. In spring, some groups of males leave the tropics and move toward the coasts of Newfoundland, Labrador and Nova Scotia. In the autumn, they rejoin the females in warmer waters.

SPECIAL FEATURES

- The whale's name refers to an old belief that its head enclosed a huge reservoir of sperm. In reality, it contains a waxy substance called spermaceti that is used to amplify and focus the volume of the sounds the whale makes, while helping the mammal to control its buoyancy. When the sperm whale makes a deep dive, the cold water penetrates through the blowhole and cools the spermaceti. As a result, the spermaceti congeals and becomes thicker, allowing the whale to descend. When the time comes to rise, blood flows to the whale's head, warming up the spermaceti and increasing buoyancy.
- A mature sperm whale can reach a depth of more than 1000 meters, perhaps more than 3000 meters. The descent and rise are rapid: up to 170 meters per minute on the way down and 140 meters per minute on the way up.
- It is generally agreed that intensive hunting during the 19th century – aimed especially at the males – upset the balance between male and female populations, which continues to aggravate the reproduction of the species.

The sperm whale has an unmistakable appearance; its huge square head measures more than a third of its total body length. It is the largest of the toothed whales.

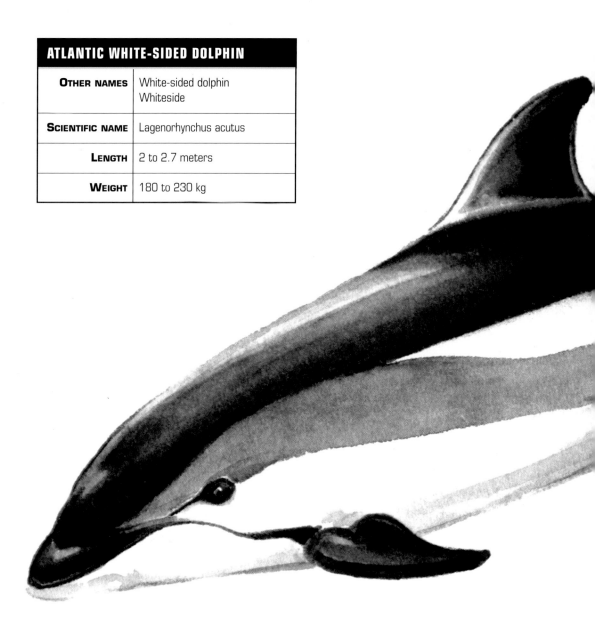

ATLANTIC WHITE-SIDED DOLPHIN

OTHER NAMES	White-sided dolphin Whiteside
SCIENTIFIC NAME	Lagenorhynchus acutus
LENGTH	2 to 2.7 meters
WEIGHT	180 to 230 kg

DURATION OF DIVE
• 1 to 2 minutes.

FOOD SOURCE
• Squid, fish (herring, capelin, sand launce, smelt, mackerel) and shrimp.

SOCIAL BEHAVIOR
• Gregarious. May be seen in large herds, numbering hundreds or even thousands of animals, moving about tightly together.

NATURAL ENEMIES

- Killer whales and some shark species are occasional predators.

HOME RANGE

- North Atlantic.
- Whitesides are abundant in the Bay of Fundy from June to October. They regularly enter the Gulf of St. Lawrence, but only rarely the estuary.

SPECIAL FEATURES

- Known for their frequent strandings. Most mass strandings involve females and their newborns, and some adult males.
- Whitesides love to swim in the wake of a boat.
- They feed on the same schooling fish as humpback and fin whales.

REPRODUCTION

- Gestation lasts between 10 and 12 months.

SURFACE BEHAVIOR

- This fast swimmer breathes every 10 to 15 seconds, by breaching or slightly breaking the water surface.

DISTINGUISHING FEATURES

- Black fins and back, white belly, gray flanks adorned with a white patch, turning to yellow or ochre.
- Short but well-defined beak.
- Huge dorsal fin, sharply pointed and curved backward.
- Small, triangular flippers located near the eyes.

White-sided dolphins are natural crowd-pleasers. They love breaching and diving head first.

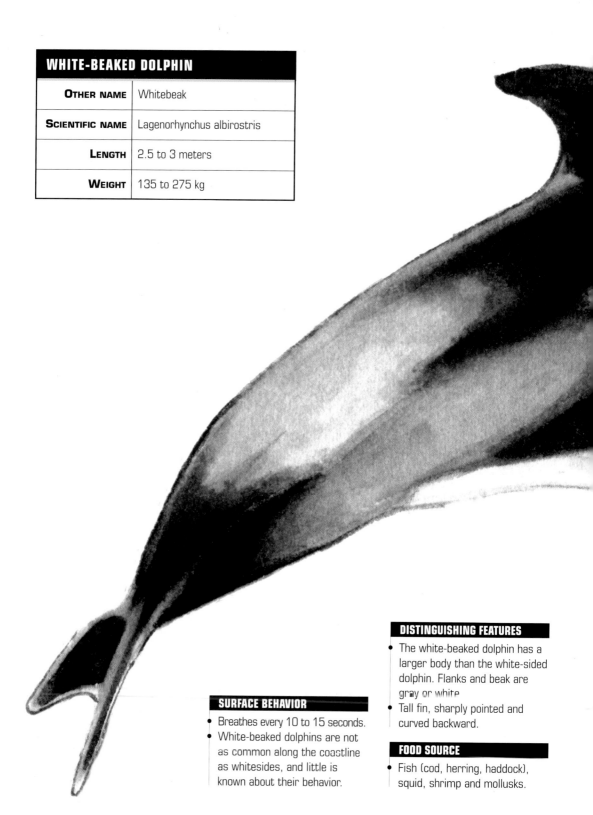

WHITE-BEAKED DOLPHIN

OTHER NAME	Whitebeak
SCIENTIFIC NAME	Lagenorhynchus albirostris
LENGTH	2.5 to 3 meters
WEIGHT	135 to 275 kg

DISTINGUISHING FEATURES

- The white-beaked dolphin has a larger body than the white-sided dolphin. Flanks and beak are gray or white.
- Tall fin, sharply pointed and curved backward.

SURFACE BEHAVIOR

- Breathes every 10 to 15 seconds.
- White-beaked dolphins are not as common along the coastline as whitesides, and little is known about their behavior.

FOOD SOURCE

- Fish (cod, herring, haddock), squid, shrimp and mollusks.

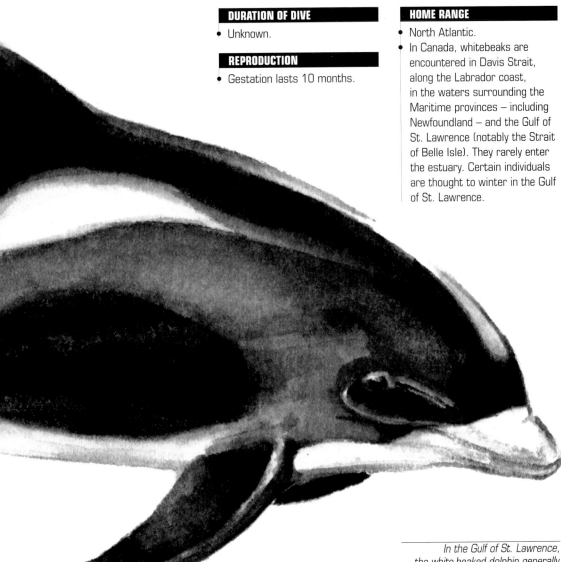

DURATION OF DIVE
- Unknown.

REPRODUCTION
- Gestation lasts 10 months.

HOME RANGE
- North Atlantic.
- In Canada, whitebeaks are encountered in Davis Strait, along the Labrador coast, in the waters surrounding the Maritime provinces – including Newfoundland – and the Gulf of St. Lawrence (notably the Strait of Belle Isle). They rarely enter the estuary. Certain individuals are thought to winter in the Gulf of St. Lawrence.

SOCIAL BEHAVIOR
- Highly gregarious, it is often spotted in groups of 2 to 30 individuals, sometimes as many as 1500.

NATURAL ENEMIES
- Killer whales and some shark species.

SPECIAL FEATURES
- Whitebeaks are exuberant, continually jumping clear of the water, splashing energetically on re-entry. These fast swimmers enjoy approaching a boat's bow so they can ride the bow wave.
- Like white-sided dolphins, whitebeaks feed on the same schooling fish as large whales.

In the Gulf of St. Lawrence, the white-beaked dolphin generally frequents the waters that are farther north than its white-sided relative.

KILLER WHALE

OTHER NAME	Orca
SCIENTIFIC NAME	Orcinus orca
LENGTH	6.5 to 7 meters; up to 10 meters
WEIGHT	3 to 7 tonnes

FOOD SOURCE

- Feeds on a rather wide range of prey: fish, squid, seals, sea lions, walruses, sea elephants, sea otters, seabirds, cetaceans (including the blue whale).

DISTINGUISHING FEATURES

- Black back with a white patch above and behind each eye and a gray "saddle" behind the dorsal fin. Part of the flanks, the underside of the flukes and the belly are white.
- Another visible feature is the tall dorsal fin. The male dorsal fin is triangular, sharply pointed and can reach 2 meters in height, while the female variety is smaller, stockier and curved backward.

SOCIAL BEHAVIOR

- Gregarious. In the Pacific, killer whales live in groups of 5 to 20 individuals, generally led by a female. Males and females remain in the same clan as their mother all their lives. Members of the same clan assist one another, especially when hunting. Little is known about North Atlantic killer whales.

REPRODUCTION

- Gestation lasts between 12 and 16 months. The baby is fed for a year, but generally follows its mother for some years. The female gives birth every 3 to 8 years.

HOME RANGE

- Worldwide. Data on Atlantic killer whales are few. They generally frequent the waters surrounding Newfoundland and Labrador, and sometimes the Maritime provinces and the Gulf of St. Lawrence.

SPECIAL FEATURES

- "Killer whale" is a misnomer, because the animal rarely attacks human swimmers, and then only accidentally.
- Among themselves, killer whales are the image of sweetness, continually nibbling, rubbing against or licking one another.

The killer whale often adopts a "lookout stance" – vertical, its head above the water.

NATURAL ENEMIES

- None.

DURATION OF DIVE

- 3 to 5 minutes;
- up to 20 minutes.

SURFACE BEHAVIOR

- Breathes 3 to 5 times on the surface. Its spout can reach a height of 4.5 meters.

PILOT WHALE

OTHER NAMES	Atlantic pilot whale Bagfin Blackfish Long-finned pilot whale Pothead
SCIENTIFIC NAME	Globicephala melaena
LENGTH	4 to 5 meters; up to 8 meters
WEIGHT	800 to 3500 kg

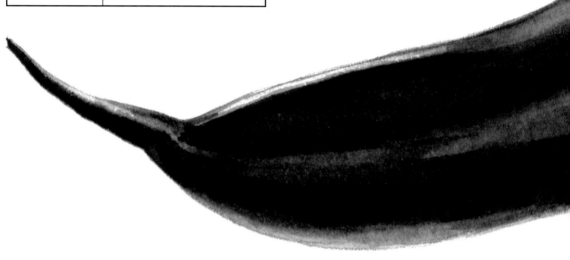

HOME RANGE

- Temperate and subarctic waters.
- In the North Atlantic, pilot whales typically follow the squid in their seasonal migrations. In spring, they venture near the coasts of Quebec – notably around the Gaspé peninsula – Newfoundland, Labrador and Nova Scotia, returning to the open sea in November.

SOCIAL BEHAVIOR

- Gregarious creatures, they live in stable groups numbering between 20 and 50 individuals.

DISTINGUISHING FEATURES

- Black or dark-brown body with a few gray spots, including an anchor-shaped patch on the throat.
- As suggested by its scientific name, the pilot whale's head is globe-shaped, or bulbous. Adult males sport a large rounded protuberance on the forehead, called the melon.
- The dorsal fin is low and large, and located in the front.
- The flippers are fine, very long and bluntly tipped.

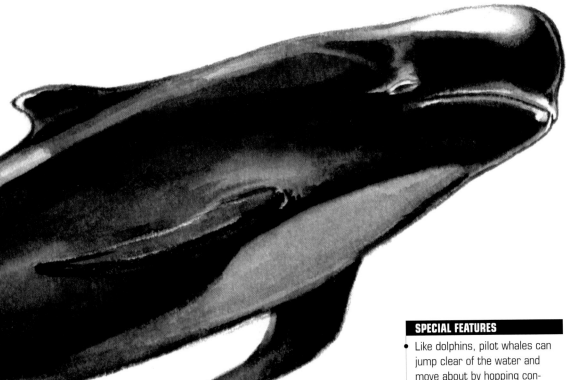

SPECIAL FEATURES

- Like dolphins, pilot whales can jump clear of the water and move about by hopping continually. They also typically adopt a vertical stance, and smack the water with their flukes.
- The species is notorious for frequent mass strandings. Between 1957 and 1980, there were 10 strandings, claiming the lives of more than 900 pilot whales.

The female pilot whale usually gives birth to a single calf. The photograph shows a female and its twins.

NATURAL ENEMIES

- Killer whales and various shark species.

DURATION OF DIVE

- 10 minutes maximum.

FOOD SOURCE

- Mainly squid, but also fish (cod, herring, mackerel, halibut).

SURFACE BEHAVIOR

- Emerges every minute or two in order to breathe, showing its melon first, then the spout, dorsal fin, back and occasionally its flukes.
- When several individuals swim, blow and dive in unison, they provide a spectacular aquatic show.

REPRODUCTION

- During mating season, males engage in duels, biting and butting one another, melon against melon.
- Gestation lasts approximately 15 months. Females give birth to a single calf every three years.

HARBOR PORPOISE

OTHER NAME	Common porpoise
SCIENTIFIC NAME	Phocoena phocoena
LENGTH	1.5 to 2 meters
WEIGHT	45 to 50 kg; up to 65 kg

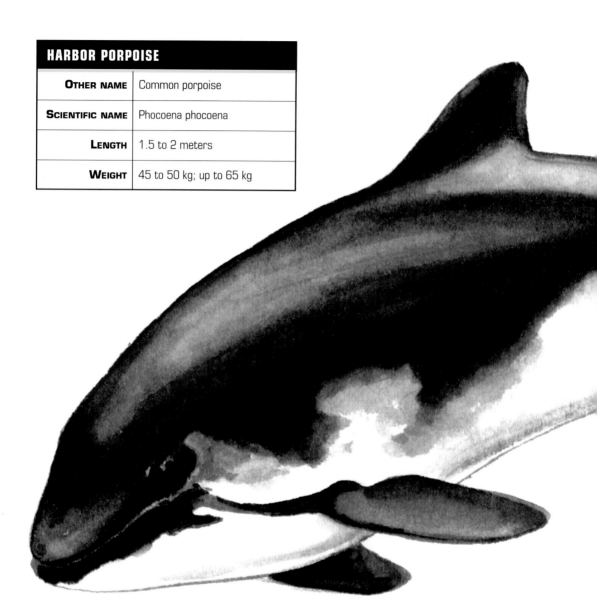

SOCIAL BEHAVIOR

- The species is gregarious, swimming alone or in pairs, but generally in a group of 5 to 10 animals. Certain herds may number several hundred individuals. When a member is in trouble, others will "jump" in to help or rescue it.

NATURAL ENEMIES

- Killer whales and sharks (Greenland and white sharks).

REPRODUCTION

- Gestation lasts 11 months. The female gives birth every 2 years, to a single calf, or sometimes twins.

DISTINGUISHING FEATURES

- Small, stocky body terminating in a round head.
- Short snout, no beak.
- Black back, grayish flanks and white belly.
- Low, triangular dorsal fin.

FOOD SOURCE

- The porpoise consumes 4 to 5 kg of food daily. It favors fish (herring, capelin, redfish, mackerel, pollock, cod, flounder), but it also feeds on squid and shrimp.

DURATION OF DIVE

- 2 to 6 minutes on average;
- up to 12 minutes.

SPECIAL FEATURES

- Timid and less playful than the dolphin, the porpoise rarely jumps out of the water, and stays clear of boats.
- Given their dark color, small dorsal fins, diminutive bodies and barely visible spouts, harbor porpoises are hard to spot in the open sea, except in perfectly calm weather.
- Each year, several harbor porpoises die accidentally in fishing nets in the Gulf of St. Lawrence and along the eastern seaboard, and in herring weirs in New Brunswick and Nova Scotia.
- The harbor porpoise was one of the first cetaceans – if not the first – to have been kept in captivity. In 1417, the French king Charles VI gave his wife, Isabeau of Bavaria, a harbor porpoise that was housed in a pool at the Hôtel Saint-Paul in Paris.

HOME RANGE

- Temperate, coastal waters in the Northern Hemisphere.
- Between spring and late autumn, porpoises can be seen in the estuary and the Gulf of St. Lawrence, as well as in the waters around the Atlantic provinces, notably the Bay of Fundy. Most porpoises leave this area in October for the open sea. Some male and young individuals stay put throughout the winter.

SURFACE BEHAVIOR

- Porpoises are very discreet; barely creating ripples as they break the water surface. They often change direction when swimming.
- As a porpoise emerges, it displays its melon first, then the back and dorsal fin.
- When hunting, it breathes four or five times, every 10 to 20 seconds, before diving. As it swims, it can spout up to 8 times in a row, at one-minute intervals.

This species is considered endangered in the northwest Atlantic.

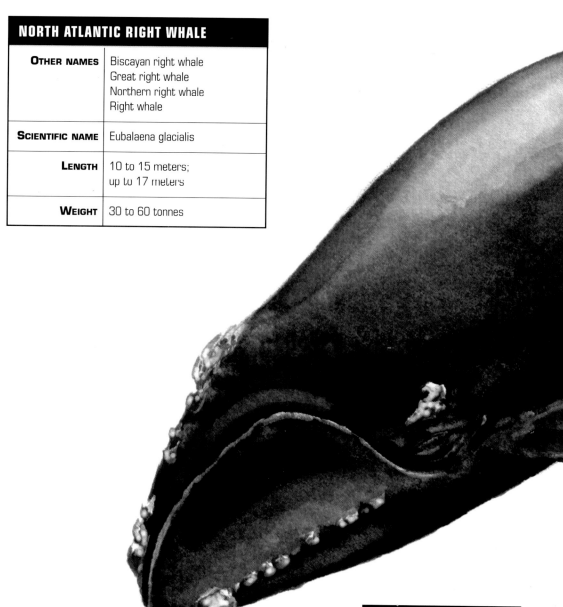

NORTH ATLANTIC RIGHT WHALE

OTHER NAMES	Biscayan right whale Great right whale Northern right whale Right whale
SCIENTIFIC NAME	Eubalaena glacialis
LENGTH	10 to 15 meters; up to 17 meters
WEIGHT	30 to 60 tonnes

FOOD SOURCE

- Filters planktonic crustaceans while swimming slowly at the surface, its mouth agape.

DURATION OF DIVE

- 10 to 20 minutes; up to 60 minutes.

SOCIAL BEHAVIOR

- Travels alone, in pairs or small groups of 4 or 5 individuals.

REPRODUCTION

- Gestation lasts 12 months. The female gives birth every 3 years. The majority of North Atlantic right whales head south in the winter for the waters off Georgia and Florida.
- The right whale has the largest testicles of any species, weighing up to 1000 kg a pair.

SURFACE BEHAVIOR

- Swims slowly at 5 or 6 km/h. When threatened, can swim off at 20 km/h.
- The whale breathes 5 or 6 times before diving. Because its nostrils are far apart, it produces a wide, V-shaped double spout. The spout can reach a height of 4 to 8 meters.
- Shows its flukes when sounding.

SPECIAL FEATURES

- The early whalers considered this species the "right" whale to capture, hence its name. Besides being a slow swimmer and more timid than other species, right whales provided hunters with great quantities of oil and baleen. Another advantage: owing to their high blubber content, right whales will not sink after being harpooned, which makes recovery easier.
- It is the world's most endangered great whale.
- This born acrobat leaps into the air and slaps the water surface with its flippers or its flukes. It can even drift along, head down and flukes out of the water.

HOME RANGE

- The waters of the North Atlantic from Florida to Labrador. They spend the winter between Cape Cod and Florida, heading north in springtime. Summer and autumn are spent in the Bay of Fundy and off the southern tip of Nova Scotia.
- North Atlantic right whales will occasionally venture into the Gulf of St. Lawrence.

The head of a right whale is decorated with rough growths – called callosities – often encrusted with barnacles.

NATURAL ENEMIES

- Only the killer whale.

DISTINGUISHING FEATURES

- Black, with white belly.
- There are large, rough growths called callosities on the snout and the head, as well as around the eyes and blowholes.
- No dorsal fin.
- Its lower jaw is strongly curved. The top of the head is wrapped on each side by the large lower lip.
- Very long baleen plates, up to 2.7 meters.

MINKE WHALE

OTHER NAME	Piked whale
SCIENTIFIC NAME	Balaenoptera acutorostrata
LENGTH	6 to 9 meters; up to 10 meters
WEIGHT	6 to 8 tonnes; up to 10 tonnes

SPECIAL FEATURES

- The animal often uses an amazing technique to capture prey, jumping straight up beneath a school of fish, with its mouth wide open.
- Sometimes it "porpoises" like a dolphin, swimming rapidly as it bounds along the surface.
- This curious swimmer often approaches boats.
- The name "minke" is said to have been coined "in honor" of an apprentice whaler who confused minkes with blue whales. Another legend has it that the same apprentice was the laughing stock on board because he overestimated the size of whales captured by his boat.

SOCIAL BEHAVIOR

- Not gregarious. Swims alone or in groups of 2 or 3. Sometimes, a few individuals may band together on or around feeding grounds.

FOOD SOURCE

- Mainly small fish (capelin, sand launce, herring) and crustaceans (krill).

DISTINGUISHING FEATURES

- Smallest baleen whale.
- Narrow, pointed head.
- Black, gray or dark-brown back, pinkish white belly.
- In the Northern Hemisphere, minkes have a white band running across each flipper, which distinguishes them from other species. (In the Southern Hemisphere, this mark is not always present.)
- Dorsal fin relatively large and hook-shaped.
- Fine, yellow baleen plates.

DURATION OF DIVE

- Up to 20 minutes.

REPRODUCTION

- Mating occurs from December to March in the North Atlantic. Gestation lasts from 10 to 11 months.

HOME RANGE

- Worldwide. Favors coastal waters and estuaries.
- In the autumn, the minke leaves the feeding grounds (estuary and Gulf of St. Lawrence, Labrador Sea, the coasts of Newfoundland and other Maritime provinces), probably heading south or out to sea, away from ice floes.

SURFACE BEHAVIOR

- As the animal emerges to breathe, it displays the dorsal fin and spout simultaneously. Though discreet, the spout can reach a height of up to 2 meters.
- After 3 or 4 breaths, the animal curves its back and dives for 5 to 10 minutes. It rarely shows its flukes.

Minke whales are abundant in the St. Lawrence River, where they live from March to December.

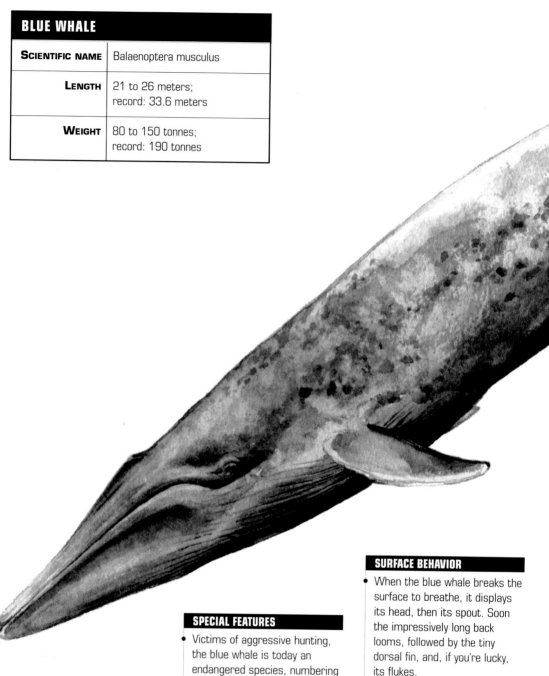

BLUE WHALE

SCIENTIFIC NAME	Balaenoptera musculus
LENGTH	21 to 26 meters; record: 33.6 meters
WEIGHT	80 to 150 tonnes; record: 190 tonnes

SURFACE BEHAVIOR

- When the blue whale breaks the surface to breathe, it displays its head, then its spout. Soon the impressively long back looms, followed by the tiny dorsal fin, and, if you're lucky, its flukes.
- The animal breathes between 8 and 15 times before sounding.
- Its spout is narrow and vertical, reaching a height of up to 12 meters.

SPECIAL FEATURES

- Victims of aggressive hunting, the blue whale is today an endangered species, numbering fewer than 1000 animals in the North Atlantic. An international agreement was signed in 1965, banning the commercial exploitation of the blue whale.

DURATION OF DIVE

- 10 to 30 minutes.

SOCIAL BEHAVIOR

- Swims alone, or in pairs.

REPRODUCTION

- Gestation lasts between 10 and 12 months. The female gives birth to a single calf every 2 or 3 years.

NATURAL ENEMIES

- Killer whales.

The St. Lawrence River is one of the few places in the world where one can observe blue whales from the shore.

FOOD SOURCE

- Tiny crustaceans (mainly krill). Consumes between 2 to 4 tonnes of food daily.

DISTINGUISHING FEATURES

- The blue whale is the largest animal (in weight and size) that has ever existed on earth. Its length is the equivalent of two tractor-trailers, and its weight equals the combined weight of to 30 elephants.
- Grayish blue with light spots.
- Large head, flat and U-shaped (viewed from above).
- Tiny dorsal fin (30 to 40 cm in height), located near the tailstock.
- Dark-blue baleen.

HOME RANGE

- Cold waters in both hemispheres. North Atlantic blue whales frequent Arctic and subarctic waters during the summer and probably winter in temperate waters.
- Most of the blue whales in the St. Lawrence generally convene just off the Côte-Nord (from Grandes-Bergeronnes to the Strait of Belle Isle), where currents and tides provide great quantities of krill.

HUMPBACK WHALE

SCIENTIFIC NAME	Megaptera novaeangliae
LENGTH	11 to 13 meters; up to 16 meters
WEIGHT	25 to 30 tonnes; up to 35 tonnes

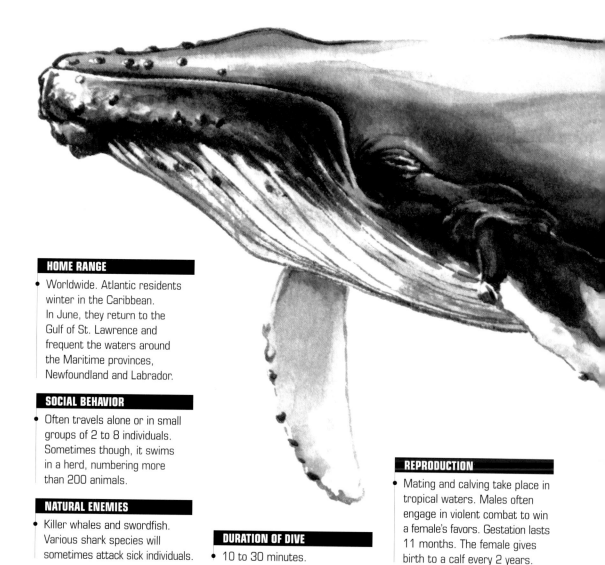

HOME RANGE

- Worldwide. Atlantic residents winter in the Caribbean. In June, they return to the Gulf of St. Lawrence and frequent the waters around the Maritime provinces, Newfoundland and Labrador.

SOCIAL BEHAVIOR

- Often travels alone or in small groups of 2 to 8 individuals. Sometimes though, it swims in a herd, numbering more than 200 animals.

NATURAL ENEMIES

- Killer whales and swordfish. Various shark species will sometimes attack sick individuals.

DURATION OF DIVE

- 10 to 30 minutes.

REPRODUCTION

- Mating and calving take place in tropical waters. Males often engage in violent combat to win a female's favors. Gestation lasts 11 months. The female gives birth to a calf every 2 years.

SURFACE BEHAVIOR

- Emerges 4 to 8 times to breathe before diving.
- Usually shows its tail before sounding. Its balloon-shaped spout can reach 2.5 to 3 meters in height.

SPECIAL FEATURES

- Humpbacks are admired for their acrobatic skill. They often jump out of the water, falling back in on their side, back or belly. They also slap the water with their tail and fins. Occasionally, they indulge in spyhopping – poking their heads out of the water at eye-level.
- The melodious chant of the male humpback is among the longest and most complex sounds ever uttered by an animal.
- Some individuals capture prey by releasing a stream of bubbles which retains the fish or krill as the whale swims upward with its mouth open.

DISTINGUISHING FEATURES

- So named because of the large hump "holding" the dorsal fin.
- The back is dark gray or black. There is a black and white patch under the tail. The belly is white, sometimes spattered with black spots.
- The flippers, too, are white, with black spots. They are very long, up to one third of the body's entire length – 4 to 5 meters.
- There are several knoblike swellings on the snout and head, each containing a stiff hair or vibrissa measuring 1 to 3 centimeters long.
- The baleen plates are dark gray or olive brown.
- The skin is often encrusted with large barnacles.

The swellings on the head of the humpback whale make it resemble a giant gherkin.

FOOD SOURCE

- Fish (herring, sand launce, capelin, mackerel) and crustaceans. It probably uses its vibrissae to assess the size of prey.

FIN WHALE

OTHER NAMES	Finback whale Razorback
SCIENTIFIC NAME	Balaenoptera physalus
LENGTH	18 to 21 meters; up to 27 meters. It is the second largest species of cetacean.
WEIGHT	40 to 50 tonnes

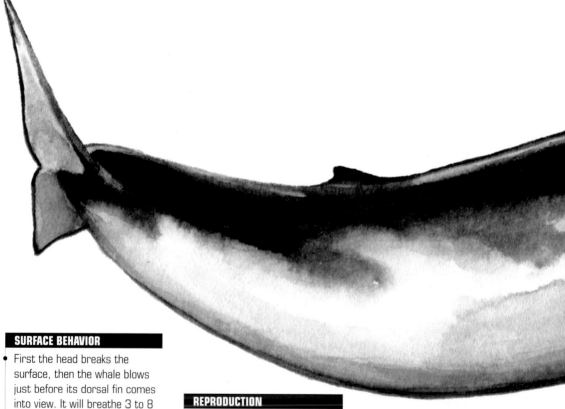

SURFACE BEHAVIOR

- First the head breaks the surface, then the whale blows just before its dorsal fin comes into view. It will breathe 3 to 8 times at intervals of 15 to 20 seconds. Rarely shows its flukes as it sounds.
- The spout is powerful and loud, shaped like an inverted cone, 4 to 6 meters tall.

REPRODUCTION

- Gestation lasts 12 months. The female bears one calf every third year. In the Northern Hemisphere, mating and calving usually take place in December or January.

SOCIAL BEHAVIOR

- Gregarious, traveling in groups of several dozen or a few hundred individuals.
- Occasionally solitary.

DISTINGUISHING FEATURES

- The back is brown or dark gray; white belly; underside of its flippers is white.
- It is the only cetacean with an asymmetric coloration: the lower jaw is dark on the left side, white on the right.
- The dorsal fin varies in shape (sickle-shaped or triangular) and is set far back. Seen from above, the wedge-shaped head is decorated with a median ridge located between the blowhole and the tip of the upper jaw.
- Its baleen is grayish blue or gray-brown, except for the anterior third of the baleen on the right-hand side, which is white or pale yellow.

SPECIAL FEATURES

- A group of 10 to 20 finbacks swimming in single file can perform an elegant aquatic ballet, diving, spouting, and arching their backs in a synchronized manner.
- They will sometimes breach, falling back on their side or belly.
- The finback is one of the fastest whales, capable of speeds up to 40 km/h.

FOOD SOURCE

- Lives mainly on krill as well as squid and fish (capelin, sand launce, herring, mackerel, cod). Finbacks ingest about 3 tonnes of food daily.

NATURAL ENEMIES

- Killer whales.

Fin whales are the most common attraction on observation tours in the St. Lawrence.

HOME RANGE

- Throughout the cold waters of both hemispheres. Migrates to the open sea or the warmer waters of the lower latitudes before ice forms.

DURATION OF DIVE

- 10 to 15 minutes;
- up to 25 minutes.

HOODED SEAL

OTHER NAME	Crested seal
SCIENTIFIC NAME	Cystophora cristata
LENGTH	2 to 2.6 meters
WEIGHT	145 to 410 kg

DURATION OF DIVE
- The seal can stay underwater up to 18 minutes.

SOCIAL BEHAVIOR
- The hooded seal is solitary, except during periods of reproduction and molting.

FOOD SOURCE
- Partial to fish (redfish, halibut, capelin, herring, cod), squid, octopus, mussels, shrimp, and will sometimes eat starfish.

NATURAL ENEMIES

- The killer whale is its main enemy. Polar bears and the Greenland shark will also attack it.

HOME RANGE

- Inhabits the Arctic and north-eastern North America. It winters on the ice floes and spends the summer off the coastlines, in deeper water.

DISTINGUISHING FEATURES

- The crest (proboscis) of the male seal is clearly visible, while the female's is small. When swollen, the male proboscis can reach a length of 30 cm and 18 cm in diameter.
- The male also has a scarlet nasal sac that resembles a balloon.
- Adult pelts are darkish gray, spotted with black on the back and sides. Face and flippers are usually black.

REPRODUCTION

- Following a gestation period of 11 ½ months (see harp seal), the female gives birth to a pup. Birthing takes place on the pack ice in March or early April. The male is polygamous, mating with 2 to 5 females each season.

SPECIAL FEATURES

- The hooded seal is an impressive diver – perhaps as deep as 350 meters – as it hunts its prey.
- The lactation period, lasting only four days, is one of the shortest in the animal kingdom.

The newborn hooded seal is dubbed "blue back" because of its silver-blue fur. This specimen is just a few hours old.

HARBOR SEAL

SCIENTIFIC NAME	Phoca vitulina
LENGTH	Varies according to region. About 1.5 meters in Western Atlantic.
WEIGHT	About 100 kg

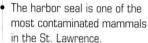

SPECIAL FEATURES

- The harbor seal is the noisiest of the St. Lawrence River seals. Besides grunting, moaning and gnashing its teeth, the seal can howl like a wolf.
- Harbor seals spend long hours resting on sandbanks and reefs uncovered at low tide. As the tide rises, they fight fiercely over the places that are still above water or dive into the water to feed.
- The harbor seal is one of the most contaminated mammals in the St. Lawrence.

DISTINGUISHING FEATURES

- The nose is short, nostrils close together.
- Limbs are short and equipped with slender, sharp claws.
- The head is small and rounded.
- The vibrissae (whiskers) are moderately long.
- Color is variable: gray blue, brown, dark or grayish yellow, covered with small dark spots and pale ring-shaped stripes. The belly is a lighter color, less spotted than the back.
- Individual animals can be recognized by the distribution of their spots.

NATURAL ENEMIES

- Sharks and killer whales are this species' main predators. In the Arctic, arctic foxes and polar bears attack the young seals.

HOME RANGE

- Along the Pacific coast, the East coast of North America (from northern Canada to Cape Cod), the coasts of Europe and northeast Asia.
- They travel up the St. Lawrence as far as Île-aux-Coudres. They're able to leave salt water and venture up rivers. In winter they frequent ice-free waters.

DURATION OF DIVE

- 3 to 7 minutes;
- up to 27 minutes.

SOCIAL BEHAVIOR

- Solitary in the water, more gregarious on dry land. During the breeding season, several hundred seals congregate on sites called "échoueries."

FOOD SOURCE

- A fish eater (herring, flatfish, smelt, mackerel, sand launce, capelin, cod, salmon, redfish), but also squid, shrimp and crab.

REPRODUCTION

- After an 11-month gestation period, the female produces a single pup. Six hours after the birth, the baby seal follows its mother into the water and swims with her. Birthing occurs in June and July in the Gulf of St. Lawrence, Labrador and Greenland. Males are usually polygamous, but don't form harems.

In profile, the harbor seal looks like a dog. Everyone is charmed by its cute face.

GRAY SEAL

OTHER NAMES	Hodge Hopper Horsehead
SCIENTIFIC NAME	Halichoerus grypus
LENGTH	1.6 to 2.3 meters
WEIGHT	Between 100 and 300 kg; up to 370 kg

NATURAL ENEMIES
- Sharks and killer whales. Young seals are sometimes the victims of adult males, seagulls, ravens and bald eagles.

DURATION OF DIVE
- 20 minutes maximum.

DISTINGUISHING FEATURES

- Profile resembles a horse.
- Widely spaced nostrils.
- Thickset body and indistinct neck.
- The adult male is a dark gray color with pale gray spots. Its flanks are a little paler.
- The female's back is gray, while its throat, belly and flanks are cream-colored, decorated with black or chocolate brown spots.
- The distribution of spots around the head help to distinguish one individual from another.

SPECIAL FEATURES

- The gray seal is one of the heftiest species. Those that inhabit Canadian waters are 20 percent larger than their European cousins.
- The gray seal adapts well to captivity, especially if taken at the age of 3 or 4 weeks. It's a common sight in zoos and aquariums.
- Like the harp seal, it has fun bobbing up and down like a cork and porpoising.

SOCIAL BEHAVIOR

- A gregarious species, especially during the breeding and molting seasons when colonies of several thousand individuals are formed.

REPRODUCTION

- Gestation lasts a little more than 11 months.
- Lactation period is 15 to 20 days.
- Northwest Atlantic gray seals breed on two types of surfaces: islands and the edges of icefields.
- The male forms harems and mates with multiple females.
- A dominant male can inseminate 6 or 7 females in a single season.

FOOD SOURCE

- Adult seals feed mainly on fish (haddock, capelin, smelt, pollock, sand launce, mackerel, salmon, skate). The young eat a diet of squid, shrimp and crab.

HOME RANGE

- North Atlantic and northern Europe.
- In Canada, it is a common species in Atlantic waters, especially in the Maritime provinces (Sable Island, Nova Scotia) and the Gulf of St. Lawrence (Anticosti Island).

The gray seal has long, narrow, curved claws.

HARP SEAL

OTHER NAME	Greenland seal
SCIENTIFIC NAME	Pagophilus groenlandicus
LENGTH	1.63 meters on average
WEIGHT	135 kg on average

FOOD SOURCE

- The harp seal's eating pattern varies according to season and region. Every year it will consume between one and one-and-a-half tonnes of fish (capelin, redfish, herring, flounder, sand launce, cod) and crustaceans (krill, shrimp).

SOCIAL BEHAVIOR

- Very gregarious.

SPECIAL FEATURES

- The harp seal is one of the three most abundant pinnipeds in the world.
- Among mammals it has a highly rapid growth rate: a baby's weight quadruples in less than two weeks.
- The harp seal can bob up and down like a cork, holding itself in a vertical position, head and upper body above the water surface before sinking down, then reappearing several times. As it swims, it can fly through the water like a dolphin.
- Older immature seals are known as "bedlamers," from the French *bête de la mer*, a phrase used by early Basque and Breton colonists of the 15th and 16th centuries.

DISTINGUISHING FEATURES

- Head is rounder than other seals and the snout is fairly short.
- Body is long, almost lance-shaped.
- The head is black and the neck white. Adult seals sport a distinctive saddle-shaped dark pattern on the back and flanks, especially noticeable in the male.

NATURAL ENEMIES

- The harp seal is highly prized by killer whales and some shark species. Polar bears prey on young seals. Walruses will occasionally kill a mother and her pup.

HOME RANGE

- Inhabits the North Atlantic and the Arctic. The migration cycle is geared to the presence of ice. Harp seals winter on pack ice off Labrador, Newfoundland and the Gulf of St. Lawrence, where they give birth, mate and molt. In spring, they travel more than 5000 km to reach their feeding grounds in the Arctic archipelago and Hudson Bay.

REPRODUCTION

- Gestation lasts about 11 1/2 months. Pupping takes place on the ice pack in February or March, lasting only a minute. The female usually gives birth to a single pup. Adult seals mate right after the young are weaned. Males are polygamous but do not form a harem.

DURATION OF DIVE

- 15 minutes maximum.
- It maintains an opening in the ice, 60 to 90 cm wide, so it can enter the water and emerge to breathe. The opening can be used by up to 40 seals.

Following pages:
Percé Rock, in the Gaspé.

Female harp seal nursing its pup. The pup is fed for a period of 10 minutes, every few hours. After 10 or 12 days the mother weans her young, which then quickly learns how to get about on its own.

Glossary

Amniotic fluid | A liquid that surrounds the embryo during pregnancy.

DDT
(dichlorodiphenyl trichloroethane) | Toxic insecticide used in the 1950s to destroy plant pests and rats.

DNA
(dexyribonucleic acid) | A nucleic acid of complex molecular structure known to play a key role in the genetic action of the chromosomes.

Echolocation | Method used by certain animals (cetaceans, bats) to detect obstacles or prey.

Gulf of St. Lawrence | An extension of the Atlantic Ocean. The Gulf "communicates" with the Atlantic via the Cabot Strait and the Strait of Belle Isle.

Krill | Shrimp-like plankton, a few centimeters long.

Mirex | Toxic product generally used as an insecticide, but also as a fire retardant in paint and paper.

Necropsy | Autopsy. The dissection and examination of a body after death.

PAH
(polycyclic aromatic hydrocarbon) | Toxic substances resulting from fuel combustion, waste incineration and the smelting of steel and aluminum.

PCB
(polychlorinated biphenyl) | Toxic substances that were used in electrical, heat-transfer and hydraulic equipment, lubricants, pigments, dyes, carbonless paper, etc. In 1980, the government of Canada banned its use in new products.

Sonar | An apparatus using sonic and supersonic waves for detecting and communicating underwater.

Sound (vb.) | Used of a fish or a whale – to dive down suddenly after the animal has breathed and curved its back.

St. Lawrence Estuary | Refers to the segment of the St. Lawrence River between Lac Saint-Pierre and Pointe-des-Monts, characterized by the presence of both fresh and salt waters.

Telemetry | A technique enabling researchers to follow and study animals – equipped with transmitters – from a distance.

Index

References

BOOKS

Beluga: a farewell to whales	BÉLAND, Pierre. New York, Lyons & Burford, 1996, 224 pages.
The life of the harp seal	BRUEMMER, Fred. Montreal, Optimum Publishing Company ltd., 1977, 174 pages.
Phoques	Collectif. Laval, Éditions Intrinsèque, 1991, 117 pages.
Les baleines de l'Atlantique Nord : biologie et écologie	FONTAINE, Pierre-Henry. Sainte-Foy, Éditions Multimondes, 1998, 290 pages.
Seals	GRACE, Eric S and BRUEMMER, Fred Toronto, Key Porter Books, 1991, 64 pages.
The whales of Canada	HOYT, Éric Camden East (Ontario), Camden House Publishing, 1994, 127 pages.
Rencontres avec les baleines du Saint-Laurent	MICHAUD, Robert. Tadoussac, GREMM, 1993, 74 pages.
Guide des mammifères marins du Canada	SYLVESTRE, Jean-Pierre. L'Acadie inc., Éditions Marcel Broquet, 1998, 330 pages.

WEBSITES

Group for Research and Education on Marine Mammals (GREMM)	**www.whales-online.net**
Mingan Island Cetacean Study (MICS)	**www.rorqual.com**
ORES Centre for Coastal Field Studies Inc., Les Bergeronnes, Quebec	**www.ores.org/**
Information on right whales in the Bay of Fundy	**www.dti-web.com/ecosystems/**
International Marine Mammal Association	**www.imma.org/**
Whale Research Group (Newfoundland)	**play.psych.mun.ca/Psych/whale.html**
Whale Watching Web	**www.physics.helsinki.fi/whale/**
American Cetacean Society	**www.acsonline.org/**
Wheelock College, Boston, MA.	**www.wheelock.edu**
Whale Club	**www.whaleclub.com/index.html**
	www.marine-mammals.com/

Photo Credits

Archives nationales du Québec (Côte-Nord) — 70, 72 bottom

Béland, Pierre, INESL — 93

Bruemmer, Fred — front cover: main photo and center inset, 14 bottom, 25 bottom, 26 top, 33, 34, 46, 49, 50, 51, 52, 66 bottom, 67, 68 top, 74, 105, 129, 144-145, 147 inset, 148-149, 149 inset, 151 inset

Caron-Boucher, Élizabeth — 13 top, 14 top, 137

Champagne, Martin — 111

Cook Church, Albert, New Bedford Whaling Museum — 69

Fontaine, Pierre-Henry — 43 bottom, 119

Lefebvre, Daniel, GREMM — 79

Maisonneuve, Charles — 18-19

Michaud, Robert, GREMM — 45 bottom, 88, 90 bottom, 92 bottom, 143

Ouellet, Marie-Claude — 78. 80-81, 100, 112-113

G. Stenson, Fisheries and Oceans Canada — 91

J.F. St-Pierre, Fisheries and Oceans Canada — 45 top

Sears, Richard — front cover (left inset), 6 top, 10, 20-21, 22, 24, 25 top, 29, 30, 38-39, 42, 44, 47, 56, 58, 66 top, 75, 76 top, 77, 86, 87, 89, 96-97, 98, 104, 114-115, 123, 125, 127, 133, 135, 139, 141

Source unknown — 64

St-Amour, Maxime — front cover (right inset), 6 center, 8-9, 16, 26 bottom, 31, 36-37, 59, 60-61, 62-63, 71, 90 top, 92 top, 101, 102, 103, 106, 110, 116, 131, 146-147, 152-153

Sylvestre, Jean-Pierre — 6 bottom, 12, 13 bottom, 15, 27, 28, 32, 40, 43 top, 48, 53, 54, 55, 57 top, 68 bottom, 73, 76 bottom, 82-83, 84, 107, 121, 145 inset, 150-151

Taber, New Bedford Whaling Museum — 72 top

Terreault, François — 35, 94-95

Vien, Lucille — 57 bottom

Contents

Ariane, age 10

Printed and bound in Canada
in March 2002
by Interglobe Inc.